Shama Naqushbandi was born in London in 1983 to parents of Kashmiri heritage. After graduating from Clare College, Cambridge University, she joined one of the world's premier international law firms and has since been working in the city. In the summer of 2011, Shama took a sabbatical to write The White House.

The White House is her first book and won 'Best Novel' in the Brit Writers' Awards 2012.

GW00778351

The White House

Shama Naqushbandi

Indigo Dreams Publishing

First Edition: The White House
First published in Great Britain in 2014 by:
Indigo Dreams Publishing Ltd
24 Forest Houses
Halwill
Beaworthy
EX21 5UU
www.indigodreams.co.uk

ISBN 978-1-909357-42-6

A CIP record for this book is available from the British Library.

Designed and typeset in Minion Pro by Indigo Dreams.

Cover design by Syed Mujtaba Rizvi. Mujtaba Rizvi is a visual artist and
Managing Director of Kashmir Art Quest. He studied at Goldsmiths,
University of London. Visit crimsonstrokes.webs.com or follow on
Twitter: @syedmmujtaba

Printed and bound in Great Britain by Imprint Academic, Exeter.
*Papers used by Indigo Dreams are recyclable products made from
wood grown in sustainable forests following the guidance of the Forest
Stewardship Council.*

Opening quotes from Agha Shahid Ali, 'Postcard from Kashmir', The Half Inch Himalayas, Wesleyan University Press and 'The Blessed Word: A Prologue', The Country Without a Post Office, W.W. Norton & Company, and Anselm Kiefer from an interview with Philippe Dagenin in Le Monde, White Cube.

But I believe above all that I wanted to build the palace of my
memory, because my memory is my only homeland.
(Anselm Kiefer)

This is home. And this the closest
I'll ever be to home. When I return,
the colors won't be so brilliant,
the Jhelum's waters so clean,
so ultramarine. My love
so overexposed.
(Agha Shahid Ali)

Let me cry out in that void, say it as I can. I write on that void:
Kashmir, Kaschmir, Cashmere, Qashmir, Cashmir, Cashmire,
Kashmere, Cachemire, Cushmeer, Cachmiere, Cašmir. Or
Cauchemar in a sea of stories? Or: Kacmir, Kaschemir, Kasmere,
Kachmire, Kasmir. Kerseymere?
(Agha Shahid Ali)

To my mother and father

ACKNOWLEDGEMENTS

There are many people without whom this book would never have been possible and I am greatly indebted to them all. Though it would be impossible for me to list them individually, I would like to mention just a few.

My mother and father for their unwavering belief in me. My twin-sister Sabah, for all her love, guidance and imagination – this book is as much yours as it is mine. My elder sister, Lara, for setting the bar so high and always pushing me to overreach myself. Ami and Papa, for their love and ceaseless prayers – just being able to read this story to you was a dream come true. My Uncle Farooq and Aunty Kounsar whose kindness, warmth and hospitality will always hold a special place in my heart. My fiancé Ishrat, for his patience, support and understanding. Dearest Tooty, for never stopping to ask for my next poem – I am only sorry it took so long. My cousin Mohsin for his brutal critique! My oldest friend, Suzanne, for never shying away from offering me a different perspective even from across the globe. The Brit Writers' Award for building my confidence to take my writing into a public forum. My publisher, Indigo Dreams, for giving me the chance to tell my story. Mujtaba, for the beautiful cover design and my editor, Pauline, for her good humour, advice and painstaking attention to detail. All my friends and loved ones, both old and new, who have supported me and believed in me throughout this process even when sometimes I did not. Last but not least, the magical children of Kashmir whose innocence symbolises all the hope and imagination of this book. This story is dedicated to each of you. I hope you enjoy the journey into The White House.

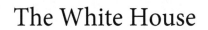

The White House

My parents were expecting two brown babies. Others who had migrated westwards found their children darkening against the new topography. So, when my sister and I arrived — pink-skinned and blue-eyed — trumpeted into the world by a Caribbean midwife who announced our entry somewhat ironically as 'Two English Roses!', they were stunned into silence. For several minutes my mother held us in her lap, searching our faces determinedly for traces of herself. Eventually she turned to my father and smiled. 'They've got the nose.'

Leila and I were born just after midday on 1 September 1983 in a hospital ward in Barking and Dagenham, London. Our names were printed in large block capitals on yellow birth certificates that my mother later entrusted to us when we left the family home. LIYANA SUQURWARDTI and LEILA SUQURWARDTI. Out of some strange deference to the rules of English grammar, my father decided to add a 'U' after the 'Q' in our surname when he came to the country, otherwise our names would have been spelt in their original form. Not that this seemed to make the slightest bit of difference, mind you. Sook-koo-wood-oo? Soo-kur-wandi? Sock-it-to you? Everybody still failed to pronounce our surname.

When I was growing up, I always felt compelled to give an explanation about my name since it was often the first thing people asked about me. Those letters perpetually preceded me. At one point, I began the tale that my sister and I had been named after contrasting times of day since I knew my name, Liyana, meant 'dawn', and my sister's name, Leila, meant 'night', in some other language, although what language it was, I was never quite too sure.

The whole thing was a fabrication though. For a start, I knew my parents had never deliberated over the poetic connotations of our names, nor, unfortunately for us, the day-to-

11

day difficulties that giving us practically indistinguishable names would inevitably cause. On the contrary, I am convinced that had they done so, foreseeing the preschool routines of fighting over the post in the morning, or the complications with setting up local bank accounts, or registering for tennis competitions, or even the possibility that a Jamaican reggae star would shoot to fame off the back of a one-hit wonder with a chorus that amalgamated both our names and to which we would be subjected in chant-like incantation for most of our adolescent years, they would have certainly garnered enough sympathy to settle upon different names. But at that time they did not think about these things. No, they did not think about these things at all. You see, the truth was, our names were not even chosen by my parents. They had, in fact, already been decided for us long before we were born.

In some strange way, my name was the first part of me that did not come from England. Instead, it came from thousands of miles away in a small landlocked valley nestled in the heart of the Indian subcontinent, a place they call Kashmir. The Valley. The rose of India's great bouquet. My paternal grandparents, who lived in Kashmir all their lives, were the ones to choose my name. Perhaps if it were possible, I would have asked them why they decided upon the name they did. Maybe one day after school I would have run into my grandmother's arms and complained, pressing her for an explanation as to why she picked such a strange, confusing name, a name which I did not understand and which nobody ever seemed to get right when she could have so easily given me a different one. But then, I suppose there would have been many other things that I would have liked to ask her too. Such things are no longer possible. You see, my grandparents passed away when I was still a small child. I cannot remember when. I cannot even say how. All I know is that they died some time long ago in this place called Kashmir.

There is nothing I would have changed about my childhood. Nothing I would have done or not done, or done differently. I grew up in privilege without want or lack. Loughton was a sleepy, white-haired neighbourhood that lay on the outskirts of London, bounded by an area of ancient woodland known as Epping Forest. It was a place of neat little trimmed lawns and leafy patios, and my sister and I grew up comfortably, swaddled in all the love that any pair of blonde, colour-coordinated twins, pushed around public parks in a double-buggy might typically expect to attract. Summers would come and go with the tinkle of ice-cream vans. And the winters — even if they had been wet and grey at that time too — well then, they were barely memorable.

Our house was a three-storey, red and white-bricked Spanish villa that lay halfway up a hill. 27 Alderton Hill. I remember it well, although it is always the garden that stands out the most. The house lay in an expanse of land that ran for several acres until it reached a few solitary compost heaps carefully hidden behind a row of sycamore trees. Halfway across the lawn stood a wooden archway trestled with ivy and climbing roses, and from the foot of the house a gravel pathway, lined on either side by flowerbeds, ran all the way up to it. In the summer, the beds over-spilled with geraniums, petunias, chrysanthemums and many other flowers whose names I did not know.

At the very back of the garden, behind the archway, there was a tennis court and it was here that my sister and I spent much of our childhood, cocooned from the rest of the world. We would carry our racquet-bags across the lawn and play for hours in that enclosure. Nobody disturbed us. Our neighbours were elderly and never seemed to venture too far from their front lawns. Sometimes our tennis balls would fly across into their back yards, and then we would take it in turns to perch on the climbing frame trying to catch a glimpse of what lay beyond those bushy boundaries. Somewhere in those depths our balls would be lost. It would always take some time before the neighbours threw them back. The balls would appear in the morning, dotted on the lawn like little fluorescent light-bulbs. Their children must have grown up and had children of their own elsewhere because I never heard the sound of other voices playing across the hedges.

In many respects, 27 Alderton Hill was the perfect sort of place for raising small children; conventional, quiet, private and unassuming, a stone's throw from the grassy parks and walkways of Essex's nature reserves. Perhaps there was plenty more sunshine back then, or perhaps it just never rains when you are a child for I can never remember it raining. Our garden was always a thick, lush quilt of greenery peppered with colourful drops and most of our early years passed as one long warm summer, just my sister and I alone. In that place, my world always ran on time. From the time in the morning when milk was delivered to the doorstep by float to the time just before bed when my mother filled two glasses with milk and I wrinkled up my nose and glugged one down. Nothing ever fell out of balance. I grew up peacefully and happily, carefree and cared for by all, and really, there was nothing exceptional or unusual that stood out about those early years ... nothing, I suppose, except the White House.

You see, the White House was the name of my grandparents' home in Kashmir. Dada and Dadi, my father's parents, had lived there for as long as I could remember, and every summer when I was little, we would pack up all our things and go to this magical faraway valley to live in a wing of their great big white house.

It lay on the outskirts, far from the walls of the inner city. There was no street number or name plaque. Everyone knew the White House.

When my grandfather first bought the land, there had

been no other homes in the vicinity. A dusty, nondescript footpath contoured to the main road and petered off, and all around, the rest of the surroundings was countryside, full of orchards, paddy, wheat and yellow mustard fields that stretched out for miles and miles running all the way down to the banks of the river Jhelum.

The property was plotted out and constructed from scratch. Bricks were carried in from an old cemetery and the walnut wood was sourced locally by a band of carpenters and carved up with steel gouges. From start to finish, the house took ten years to complete because my grandfather did not have enough money to do it in one go. Dada was a judge and often travelled to different provinces with his work, now and then returning with various items for the house, like the Buddhist prayer wheel from Ladakh encrusted with semi-precious stones, or the patchwork *Bakarwal* carpet that hung from the wall in the landing, a purchase from a family of nomadic shepherds. When the building was finally complete, it resembled something like a large country manor. It was a tall and solemn-looking structure, imposing and upright in the image of my grandfather. Dada was a stickler for cleanliness and even in the bitterest of winters, the curtains were always drawn apart and the windows flung open.

'Let the air in!' he would command the workers each morning and all day long, cool fresh air blasted through the house.

People called it the White House because the exterior was painted white. It was a pristine white, white like the colour of milk or fresh snow, or white like a blank sheet of paper. Even when more homes sprung up and the area grew to become a prosperous residential district, they struggled to vie with its presence. Its white colour gave it a certain specialness, setting it apart from the rest, and, I suppose, over time the name stuck.

If the outward appearance of the White House brought to mind the strict, ascetic character of my grandfather, then

15

inside, it was the gentle, velvety warmth and soft luxuries of Dadi, my grandmother, which took over. A natural warmness ensconced my grandmother wherever she went, somehow almost magically deepened by the earth-coloured shawls she draped around herself. Every so often, she would draw the shawls in more tightly and the material would ripple, surging forth like a sea, sometimes burying me in a womb of pillowy fabrics if I was still sitting on her lap. My grandmother came from one of the richest families in the Valley and it was said that on her wedding day, her dowry was carried in by four men in an enormous paper-mâché crate that had taken over nine months to paint. The same chest lay in the bedroom where my sister and I slept and it was the sort of piece you could sit quietly and stare at for hours without ever getting bored. I used to run my fingers along the loops and curls trying to spot the birds hidden away in the craftwork. The more I searched, the more bulbuls seemed to fly out from the artistry.

In many ways, the White House was everything that Alderton Hill was not. If Alderton Hill was quiet and secluded, the White House was a constant bustle of activity and aromas, full of people and chatter. It was a home where young cousins grew up together, and grandparents had their grandchildren close by. Activity would surface early in the morning when, for at least a couple of hours, a small crowd gathered in the courtyard while a special brown rice was dispensed from a piping-hot vat. One of the workers would sit before the vat all morning stirring the rice and distributing it with a large pewter spatula while my sister and I looked on.

With the deepening of the morning sun, the entrance gate would begin to clang as relatives arrived and it would not be long before an endless line of uncles and aunts filed in to commence a ritual of cheek-pulling, hair-ruffling and eyeballing; sometimes doing all three together. Every now and then, the rattle of a tea trolley followed follow. As more visitors arrived, a neat stack of shoes piled up outside the front door. The rituals would continue without pause throughout the day until eventually my cousins came by, and then my sister and I would escape with relief to play with them in the garden outside.

If our garden in Alderton Hill stood out, then what waited for us at the White House made it pale into a pot-plant by comparison. Surrounding all sides of the house was a vast expanse that ran for stretches, full of trees that were forever bursting with blossom and ripe fruit.

'Everything good in the world can grow here', my uncle once said and I think he must have been right because I used to think that all the fruits of the world grew in that garden: apples, pears, cherries, plums, grapes, pomegranates, mulberries, peaches, apricots, walnuts, almonds ... almost everything I loved grew in that place.

In the afternoon, chairs would be set up in the shade of an old chinar tree and beneath that canopy my grandmother would serve fruit. My cousins would take it in turns to climb the apple trees and shake off their load while Leila and I waited at the bottom, catching the falling fruit.

'Catch Liyana! Catch!' I would spin around with my arms outstretched as the apples fell one by one.

At the end, we would carry the best of our pickings to my grandmother and she would peel the skin for us. Fruit always seemed to taste best when it came plucked fresh off a twig.

When evening came I would curl up in Dadi's lap in front of the television, wrapped in her woollen shawls, and watch old Bollywood movies. One evening it was Dilip Kumar — the great tragic heartthrob — bellowing down the Himalayas. The next evening, it was Monica shimmying voluptuously in a water-logged sari under Monsoon rains. Although I struggled to understand the words, I would follow the changing colours and costumes in silent fascination, waiting for the moustachioed villains to be vanquished and the lovers to be reunited. In this way, without even realising it, I came to know all the great classics of Indian cinema. My father told me that many of the movie stars had passed through the doors of the White House when he was a boy. In the summer months, they would come escaping the heat and dust of the southern plains and stay in the wings, renting the spare rooms.

'Raj Kapoor came, and Vyjayanthimala too, after shooting Honeymoon. Even Rekha came', my father said, 'though she was just a girl back then, not even famous at that time!'

Back then, the Valley was the film-set of choice and countless love-songs were cooed against the backdrop of its steep sweeps and scenic drops. I remember watching a black and white film about a man who was haunted by the ghost of a girl. She sang to him from swings and carousels across the mountain ranges and then vanished without a trace. The hero had followed her voice, lovelorn. As the camera swooped across smoky footbridges and balconies, he called out to her from behind the jewelled grills of an outdoor pavilion like it was a golden birdcage.

Somewhere in between those lullabies, I fell asleep and my grandmother picked me up, cradling me in her warmth and carried me gently to bed. When I grew up, I could never remember the name of that film, although I tried many times to find it.

In the Valley, I lost all sense of time. The White House was my summer playground, my doorway to another world, a faraway land I could step in and out of, like one of those places in Enid Blyton's book about the magical tree. It was a place that made me feel special. Everything seemed magnified in that house. A whole family waited for me there, a family I never saw for the rest of the year. And each year we returned, they opened their arms to us. Parties would be thrown in rainbow-coloured gardens, and huge marquees would parachute up, quilted in the

18

paisleys and dancing vines of Kashmiri carpets. Every day, my sister and I played with our cousins, chasing one another around the trees and rosebushes of that great garden. Once we even went pony-trekking in the mountains and I rode a beautiful caramel-brown pony called Honey. The *pony-wallah* swung his legs over its strong body and galloped us across the daisy-filled meadows. I cracked the reins as we raced forward, yodelling and hallooing in excitement. I was sure I was flying.

I cannot remember how long I spent in the Valley. Perhaps it was weeks, perhaps months, perhaps even more. Sometimes I think it must have gone beyond the summers. Out there, things simply followed the rise and fall of seasons and somehow, I felt I had known and seen them all. There was a natural continuity to life. As the bitter Himalayan cold subsided, the migrating birds would return to the White House signifying the coming of spring and with that first sign of the turning of the season, a lovely smell would fill the air, imbuing the garden with a new zest. It was the smell of pink lilacs and yellow daffodils and all kinds of pretty fragrant flowers. An assortment of colourful chirping birds followed, reinvigorating the world around me and I would carry on heedlessly, darting in and out among the throng of relatives, barely appreciating the subtle changes unfurling all around me. But always, in her favourite spot, I would catch sight of Dadi, sitting timeless and perfect like a portrait, beneath the shade of the chinar tree. Even under a spray of sunlight, somehow she still managed to look so wonderfully earth-coloured.

When it came to her medication time, just before bed, I would giggle at my grandmother's pronunciation of 'spoon'.

'Sup-poon,' she would say.

I would laugh at her strange pronunciation and mimic the sound back to her. Dadi would smile.

'You have forgotten me,' she would say half in protest.

19

'You have forgotten me.'

And her eyes would sparkle like they were laughing too. I did not know my grandparents for long. People tell me I have my grandmother's temperament. Many years later, after they passed away, I discovered I had been put on a diet as a baby, and my grandmother used to feed me sugar lumps when nobody was looking.

If childhood is a garden, I think mine must have drifted across the earth like one of those floating blossom beds I had seen on the lake in the Valley with their open shacks. Somehow they never sank. In the midst of the grassy marshland, the lake-children hopscotched between different islands dodging the hanging marrows and waterlilies. My home was as fluid as theirs. Alderton Hill and the White House; the two clods of earth were connected. No distinctions were made. Each home was as welcoming as the other. My parents would dress us in Kashmiri outfits in England and English outfits in Kashmir. Back then, the two wardrobes were interchangeable. Leila and I moved effortlessly between them, as naturally as migrating birds might move between the changing climes.

Returning from the Valley, I carried with me a treasure-trove of stories, and each time I would take these tales, like little trinkets, to the place where they seemed to gravitate best. Ami and Papa were my mother's parents and the first Kashmiris to settle in England. Up in Manchester, they were our gatekeepers to an incomprehensible past that found its definition in foods and smells and soft felts. There was something magical about Ami and Papa. Although they never joined us in our trips to the Valley, they seemed to know everything about the place, as if its very slopes and bends ran deep like the web of veins branching out across the back of their hands. My grandfather had been born into one of a handful of titled, landowning families in the Valley, hailing from the apple-growing region where farmers and tillers had ploughed the fields for generations. I used to think this was why he knew that patch of earth so well, for at times when Papa spoke of growing up in a vast rural estate over-spilling with people, it seemed as if he was just describing another White House.

Papa was a great storyteller, and Leila and I would spend hours nestled in the nooks of his sofa listening as his voice carried us back to a time more astonishing and miraculous than the world of fantasy and make-believe, more enchanting than the Floating Island of Laputa with its lonely robot gardeners and levitating pendants, more moving than the Last Unicorn with its crescendo of stallions emerging en masse from the white surf of the tide. The things my grandfather spoke of touched me with a sense of unparalleled wonder. I was able to imagine them perfectly. Without pictures or animation, I came to know about all the different characters who worked on his ancestral land: the bookkeepers, the artisans, the bakers, the *kangri*-makers, the farmers, the potters, the shoemakers, the religious peers, the cattle-breeders, the odd-jobbers, the *Pandits* …

'So many people lived and worked on the land, Liyana,' Papa would say, his face lighting up with expression. 'So many hundreds, I cannot remember their names!'

And each time he spoke of that ancient world, I would listen, drawn in, not wanting his stories to end. There was something extraordinary about the way Papa could delve into a seemingly bottomless storehouse of memories and transform them into tales of boyish adventure. My grandfather knew all the dates, the times of day, the sounds, the smells, the textures, every minutia down to what cloth the baker's son was wearing, and the colour of his first bicycle, and it was as if, when he conjured that bygone world, for several moments it existed once more, brought back and pieced together for us, in the intimacy of his living room in the north of England.

21

'Carry on, Papa! Carry on!' I would implore, tugging at his jumper whenever he paused to take a sip on his tea.

And then he would smile and tell me once more about his school days, like the first time he was introduced to England, and how the schoolmaster called his name from the register and summoned him into a small office. Inside the room sat a large wooden desk and, hanging above it next to a portrait of the Maharaja, an enormous multi-coloured map of the world.

'The schoolmaster pointed to a small island in the middle of a big, blue expanse and told me that this was where our rulers came from. "English people don't waste time," he said, "Even when they take their tea, they take it in a bottle!"'

And from the master, my grandfather learnt that Englishmen were good and clean, and never looked dirty like the villagers in the Valley. Bit by bit, Papa learnt how an Englishman ate, how he cleaned, how he dressed, and all his other peculiar habits and oddities.

'They were like a fairy tale to us,' he laughed, reeling me deeper and deeper into the past, as he described how one of his class-fellows once returned from a trip to the city at night, wide-eyed in wonder, convinced that he had just witnessed a group of white ladies dance naked before him. They had spun on the decks of the houseboats like dervishes under the moon, their pale skin sparkling in the twilight. My grandfather chuckled, remembering how his friend had been unable to fathom a better explanation for their night-time revelry and silken evening gowns.

And of course, through those stories, I came to know how Papa met Ami. Papa was sixteen when the marriage was arranged. As one of fourteen children, his father considered it expedient to marry his sons in pairs, and so my grandfather was wed at the same time as his younger brother. The wedding was a lavish affair with several months of feasting, and well-wishers came to the house from all across the village. A temporary holiday was declared allowing the workers to enjoy the festivities also, and labour on the land ground to a halt. In the evenings, the womenfolk gathered indoors to sing songs of praise, rocking back and forth in unison as musicians played long into the night. Halfway through the ceremony, Papa's brother fell asleep on the marriage dais and needed to be plied with sweetmeats to be kept awake. On the final day of the celebrations, my grandmother arrived wearing a dark-red bridal dress intricately woven with gold *Zarbafth* threads, decorated in matching jewellery. The veil was so heavily embellished that some of the women gasped when she entered, whispering that it could have been melted to a great weight of gold.

Ami was only thirteen when she married.

'My mother told your Ami she was too young to be a daughter-in-law. And when your Ami asked if she could go home when the celebrations were over, she just kissed her on the forehead.' My grandmother bent down and kissed me gently on the forehead replicating the action as Papa continued. 'What could she do? Such things just happened then.'

For the next several years, as the land was tilled and harvested in turn, my grandmother spent her time at leisure playing with Papa's younger sisters at the bottom of the orchards. At the very back, a wooden swing hung from a bough of an apple tree and while Papa was away, she would swing on it for hours.

'Carry on, Papa! Carry on, Papa!' Leila sister would squeal excitedly, eager for more tales, and we would tuck ourselves in closer, sinking deeper into the sponginess of that sofa, every now and then sipping on the saffron tea that Ami poured for us into her pink Wedgwood cups. Just before she did so, Ami would scatter a handful of almond flakes into the cups, and Leila and I would watch in silence, as if watching a fairy godmother cast some magic spell.

Ami never sat still. A Ferris wheel of activity, she bustled in and out of the kitchen constantly spoiling us with all sorts of exotic treats. No one could cook *tabak-maaz* better than my grandmother. The crispy fried lamb ribs tasted just like they had come straight out of the *Waza's* cooking pots in Kashmir. And as we listened to Papa's tales, my grandmother would come and go in a swirl of kaleidoscopic colour, a cascade of moving tints and hues, continuously beaming and repeating 'love-el-ly' to everything we said as if it was some special word. Sometimes she would shower us with endearments in a foreign tongue we did not understand.

'Do you know what your Ami is saying?' Papa would ask, and we would look back sheepishly with blank faces. 'Don't you know what your Ami is telling you?' my grandfather would repeat crumpling his brow in mock-incredulity. 'Why, girlies, your Ami is saying she would sacrifice herself for you!'

It was not until much later, when I was old enough to understand, that I learnt my grandparents had been on the wrong side of the border when lines were drawn on a map, and a funnel-shaped piece of land formerly known as British India was carved up into two separate states: India and Pakistan. The Valley which was situated between the two eventually fell under Indian control, although remained hotly contested by Pakistan. For my grandparents, the birth of the two nations came at a colossal price.

'You might as well give up,' a hard-nosed official at the immigration desk told my grandfather after tiring of his repeated visits. 'They'll never let you back!'

Stranded in a place where no one knew who they were or the life they came from, my grandparents suddenly found themselves joining a heaving mass of anonymous, struggling refugees, swathes of estranged humanity migrating across the borders from Jalandar, Amritsar, the Punjab, Bihar, and all the other place-names over a lacerated continent that had gradually begun to swell into one. What brought about the partitioning of that land and people, I never fully understood. How it unfolded had been carefully censored even from my grandfather's imagination. All I knew was that in this new country, Pakistan, my grandparents lost everything: their family, their friends, their influence, their status built up over a rota of kind centuries, their home. Even my grandmother's bridal gold once so proudly displayed on their wedding day when the women linked arms and sang with wet eyes, got left behind, lost somewhere between the sliding corridors of time. My grandparents moved into a shared home with several other families and went on to use the same bedding for the next few years. When the opportunity arose, they flew out to England, nationless, on documents that identified them as 'citizens of the disputed territory of Jammu and Kashmir'.

It was not until over twenty years later that Papa was able to return to the Valley again, and perhaps such a thing might never have been possible had he not, this time, travelled under the aegis of one of those fair-skinned, fairy-tale women, as a British citizen.

But by the time my grandfather returned alone, things had soured in the Valley. Partition had decimated the old trade route that was once the very lifeblood to his family's wealth. At home, he found the great storerooms and urns of the old estate filled with rotting grain. Unprecedented land reforms had struck a further blow to his family's fortunes, wiping out much of their ancestral affluence overnight. Whether the people had diseased the land, or the land had diseased the people, my grandfather could not tell, but one thing was certain, the sickness had spread its contagion to those most close to him. His mother was dying of cancer. Barely two days passed when armed tribals crossed over the border into the Valley and a new uprising began, forcing my grandfather to leave for a second time. However, this time it was for good. Not long after, both his parents passed away. Their graves were dug only a few metres from the estate where he had grown up.

In his absence, the remaining brothers divided up what

was left of the property. One by one, the ornaments and hangings were taken down, the upholstery sold and the great mansion stripped of its value. A travelling merchant bought the Belgian chandelier that hung majestically in the hallway, disappearing without a trace. It took some time before the news filtered back to England that my grandparents had been left nothing in the inheritance, not even a home to return to. It was almost as if by being in England, they had somehow ceased to exist in the Valley.

I stopped going back to the White House when I was six or seven. I cannot remember exactly when. Everything I had known there got left behind.

'Do you remember who I am? You don't remember me? Can't you remember who I am?' my relatives would complain many years later.

Many of the clothes I used to wear — the colourful woollen shrouds, the blue velvet waistcoats with curling gold-rimmed mirror-work, and the pretty hand-embroidered caps — were outgrown and promptly packed into a large bin-liner and sent off to the local charity shop. The two old ladies behind the counter thanked my mother with honeycomb smiles. Even my favourite jumper — a woollen cardigan, a gift from Dadi — was locked up in a suitcase and buried away somewhere in the attic, forgotten. I was too young to notice what was happening. It just happened. Nobody told me why, and I guess I was careless and easily distracted at that age too, because I did not ask why either.

Back in Alderton Hill, another world was already opening its gates to me. I felt it coming around the corner. And this time, there were other children. Many other children. They came pushing and shoving, clinging to the ankles of their parents, wearing red berets and pinafores, new, shiny and clean, filing into the classrooms virtually indistinguishable from one another. When school began, it signalled the start of something new. Something exciting. Our garden in Alderton Hill slowly began to open up like a buttercup. Half-curious and half-reluctant, I was pushed forward to greet the other children. A new world was unravelling around me, and like the rest of the nervous, twitching children queuing up outside the school tuckshop with their parents on that first day, I was ushered forward with it.

When my mother took me into the tuckshop, a pinched-face woman behind the counter took out a roll-up tape and measured me for my uniform. Several hours later, we left with two huge bags full of blouses, skirts, pinafores, berets and blazers. That evening, my mother sewed little cotton tags stencilled with my name onto every item of clothing. Not an item went unlabelled. Even my panties were labelled, my name neatly tucked inside the rim just in case I might forget. My school bag, pencil-case and stationery were labelled too, the letters running in a long line like the alphabet, a seemingly endless trail of capitals. Everything was labelled. I went to school wrapped in my name. It was as if my mother knew all along that people would be fascinated by it. They would stare at it in school registers and lean over my workbook, trying to follow syllable after syllable. They would slur as they tried to pronounce it. They would abbreviate it. They would ask me where it came from as if somehow it was separate to me. I would have to stand up and introduce it. I would have to spell it out loud. I had to write it at the top of the page at least ten times a day. I was always the last to finish writing it. People pronounced it in so many different ways, I began to forget how to say it. I began to feel at odds with my name. I didn't understand it. It was too long. Too bulky. Too clumsy. Too different. It didn't flow. A group of boys began chanting it. I started to dislike it. I hated it. Why had I been given it? A mistake had been made.

'Miss, I think a mistake has been made!' I was convinced

a mistake had been made. Somebody had got it wrong.

With the beginning of school, something changed. The Valley left our lives. The trips back to the White House and the evenings curled up in front of the TV watching old Bollywood classics with Dada and Dadi stopped. It all disappeared. With that secret garden now gone, all that remained was our English garden, and it was in this garden, all of a sudden brought to the forefront of our reality, that my sister and I rooted and began to grow. With our fair skin and light eyes, we blended in effortlessly, camouflaged in uniform against the rest of the girls in our class. We conformed almost unconsciously, caught up in the novelties of the present. Perhaps somewhere far away, someone may have shook their head in disappointment. Someone may have objected or spoken out, perhaps said our world shrank a little, that maybe the colours lessened, the smells changed, the sun burned a little less brightly than before. Perhaps some such voice of doubt would have said something like that ... but the truth was, I never noticed it. I never noticed it at all. So even when, many millions of miles away in a small, far-off valley, the steeples blared out the mourning call of two souls whose embrace I had once so intimately known, and men with Biblical faces gathered in congregation to bend their heads in prayer, 'To God we belong and to Him we shall return,' the news passed me by as softly as a falling leaf. What I was doing at that time, I cannot say. What I would have felt had I known, I suppose I shall never know. All I know is that the path to take me back to that distant valley had vanished from the back of my garden. It had been pulled so swiftly and so early on that even my memories had been too fledgling to crystallise in time for it. There was nothing to connect me back to that place anymore. In England, time moved forward from stamp collections to marble collections to sticker collections, and, in the end, really, it was only my name that gave me away.

School forced everyone to venture outdoors. At the sounding of the bell, the teachers slammed their books shut and with a sigh of relief released the kids outside. No one was allowed to stay inside. Not even in the winters when it snowed in flakes or the sleet hailed down hard and left red marks on your skin. Stragglers would be picked up on patrols, pulled up from beanbags and locker-rooms or from under stairwells, and systematically frog-marched outside. There were no exceptions. It was a rule that was meticulously enforced. Everyone had to go outside. In the playground, another reality lay in wait. At times, it was a rough and callous reality, unregulated by the order and discipline that lay within those warm, heated classroom walls. The playground had its own groups, rules and systems and it did not take long for me to realise that popularity was premised on numbers. Groups were formed, alliances built, fights waged and armistices declared. The bigger kids pursued the smaller kids. The smaller kids harangued the bigger kids. The runaways tried to escape, jumped off walls, broke things and ended up in bins. Some got splinters on their fingers, others, cuts on their shins or bruises on their bottoms. But always before the sounding of the second bell you had to brush the dirt off and pull yourself back together again in time for the next lesson. It was all part of the education.

'YOU'RE IT!'

The first day, when I walked through the school gates dressed in my freshly-ironed uniform, I saw a girl with blonde plaits being chased across the playground. She looked like Rapunzel, racing past swings and roundabouts, fleeing in a frenzy with her hair jumping up and down behind her, until a chubby-fingered boy tricked her with a turn and she ran straight into him. A podgy fist grabbed her plaits tugging them like a pony.

'Gotch-you!' he squealed in excitement, and suddenly she was left standing there, frozen, arms up and legs spread, zapped into surrender, the boy gloating over her like a tyrant. She looked at me as I hurried on past unable to save her.

In the school office, across the top of a large desk I could barely see over, one of the teachers shook hands with my mother. I could not hear what was said, but afterwards my mother nodded, bent down to kiss me, and then left. Moments later, Leila and I were split up and my sister put in a different class. In an instant, I found myself alone with our joint snack box. It contained two peaches, one for Leila and one for me, and my mother had entrusted it to me for the both of us.

'Such an exciting time!' I heard her breathe before leaving.

But I wanted to be with my sister and didn't understand why we had been separated. I fought back tears of confusion. As I lined up to be counted for my first morning assembly, two girls, one a slim, mousey-looking brunette and the other, a tubby blonde, grabbed my hand and squeaked in unison, 'Be my friend?'

I quickly made friends with them both.

The first thing I learnt at school was that mine was full of Jewish kids. The two girls I made friends with were Jewish too. None of us ate sausage rolls at lunchtime and it was automatically assumed that I was Jewish too. Sandwiched between them, I was ushered into Jewish assembly and would sit by the radiator at the back of the class listening to a man in a long black cloak and top-hat read out rhymes. He spoke with such theatricality that at first I mistook him for a magician. My sister seemed to encounter the same treatment too. One time, we were waiting by the bus stop when a lady approached us and insisted that we accompany her to a nearby Jewish centre. Leila and I looked at one another, confused, not knowing what to say, but the lady insisted, even asking us where our parents came from.

'Ah Kashmir! Yes, I know Kashmir. Now which part of Israel is that again?'

Unfortunately though, the attention we received for our Semitic looks was not always so benevolent.

'Jews! Jews!'

A group of boys that loitered outside our local tennis centre thought we were Jewish too and shouted names at us whenever we walked past. Most days our father would pull up at the front entrance of the centre and we were lucky enough to avoid their name-calling, but sometimes if he was running late for work, he would drop us off at the back gate to the sports grounds, and then we would have to walk through a field to get to the centre. I dreaded those walks, knowing we might cross the path of those boys smoking outside. They were much older than us, and unlike the kids with memberships at the centre, did not come to play sport at the club. Whenever we passed I would try to avoid looking at them but I had seen that some had shaved heads, and their trainers were torn. One afternoon, when we were approaching the centre, a brick hurtled through the air, shattering a glass window just metres from my head. After that, I became very afraid of looking Jewish. I would tell Leila to take the racquet from her sports bag whenever we walked through that field just in case we had to run.

And yet, despite this, part of me was curious about the identity that had been mistakenly thrust upon us. There was something about it that compelled me, something that deeply intrigued me.

What did it mean to be Jewish? Was it something biological that came from the blood, or was it something you felt in the heart? Did it come from the mind? Did it come from the gut? If neither, where did it come from? What was it that made me different from my friends?

In our library, I began scouring the children's section for books on Judaism, reading stories about the history of the Jews and their migrations through time, trying hard to bottom out what it meant to be one of the 'Chosen People'.

At school, on Jewish holidays, the classrooms were always half-empty and at one point it seemed as if everyone was

31

celebrating a Bar Mitzvah or Bat Mitzvah. Deep down, I longed to be invited. The girls would talk about them during lesson-breaks and I would try to imagine what it was like being a part of one. I heard you received lots of presents and there was a special cake. And so it hurt inside when neither of the girls I befriended on my first day invited me to their Bat Mitzvahs. They shrugged apologetically when they told me and joked with one another in a language I did not understand, and I suppose that was the first time I became conscious of a lack of sorts. I remember wishing I could speak another language too, but my parents had only ever raised me to speak English. In the end, I passed through primary school without ever going to a Bat Mitzvah or trying the special cake.

My family was not Jewish. We were Muslim. Though I never saw my father go to the mosque or prostrate himself on a prayer mat, I never questioned otherwise. It did not matter to me that he did not have a beard and occasionally sipped on gin and tonic when we went to our local Chinese restaurant for crispy Peking duck.

Dada, my grandfather, had been a very religious man and I remember our dressing-up box held several embroidered skullcaps that he used to wear when praying. In the living room of the White House, there had been a large walnut wood bookcase that contained Dada's old Persian books on poetry and law. Of all the things in the White House, it was said these books were his most prized possessions and he would keep them carefully preserved in purple velvet covers, tightly stacked next to one other. On the same bookcase, there was a photo-frame that contained a piece of paper etched with a genealogical tree tracing our family's lineage all the way back to the last Prophet. To be descended from the Prophet, someone once told me, was a very special thing.

'When people send their prayers to the Prophet and his

family, it means that they are sending their blessings to you too.'

And I had listened quietly, thinking how strange it was that people could attach such importance to something that felt so far away.

Like many of the men in Kashmir, with their aquiline features and stately looks, Dada had acquired a sort of Abrahamic aspect with age. Every day he would wake at dawn, shower with an ice-cold bucket of water and pray until just after ten o'clock. Whenever he travelled into the city, he would spend the whole bus journey bent over his beads in devotion. He wore dark glasses, and it was a habit that often attracted the attention of his fellow passengers until eventually one asked why he covered his eyes. My grandfather removed his glasses and showed the man that his eyes were wet with tears.

'His faith was so strong,' people would say each time they told me the story. And they would suck deeply at the air as if to stress the point. 'So strong!'

Although Dada had been a strict father, he had never forced religion on any of his children, and as a boy my father only ever accompanied him to the mosque for *Shab-e-Barat* where he and his brothers would spend a special night in the year sleeping at the local shrine. The shrines in the Valley fascinated me when I was a child. I would spot them sitting on the highest hilltop or carved out in the remotest wood, their gates covered with thousands of coloured threads that people had knotted and left, only to be untied once their prayers were answered. Perhaps part of the intrigue came because my mother disapproved of them. She would find it uncomfortable watching the local women rocking back and forth, weeping and wailing as they clung to the columns of the mausoleums. Once when Leila started to imitate them, she had pulled us away and insisted we leave straightaway.

'You do not need others to access God,' my mother told us firmly.

After my grandfather returned from the Hajj pilgrimage,

perhaps he realised the same thing too, because his visits to the shrine stopped and he would only pray at the mosque on Fridays. As a result, my father never really had any formal religious education when he was growing up. He was never taught how to pray. In the same way then, I guess, my father adopted a similar approach when it came to us, and really it was only thanks to my mother that I was taught how to pray.

When we were little, Leila and I would sit tucked up together in the duvet of our double-bed, in headscarves, while my mother recited the *Quran*. She taught us a few of the prayers, breaking the Arabic sounds into monosyllables for us to recite back.

'Wa! Ta! Ba!'

I would repeat the words, twisting my mouth into all sorts of contortions overzealously attempting to imitate the more guttural of the sounds. Arabic sounded funny and strange. I would look at my sister dressed in my mother's flowery silk headscarves, not really understanding what I was saying, struggling to take the lessons seriously. I could tell Leila was thinking the same. Our faces twitched as we both tried to out-concentrate our giggles and it would not be long before one of us broke into laughter. To my mother's exasperation, the effect was always contagious and within moments the two of us would be rolling about the bedcovers in a fit of chuckles. My mother would get cross, straighten her back and firmly fold her arms.

'We can't help it, Mama,' we would titter. 'It sounds funny!'

But once the humour subsided, Leila and I would sit up again, fix our headscarves and the recitation would begin once again.

My mother tried her best and I will always love her for it. Teaching Leila and I about religion was one of the few things she insisted upon, despite my father. There was no mosque in our area, only a synagogue and the local church, and so on Saturday mornings, she would make the journey with us into Central London to the largest mosque in the country. Regent's Park Mosque held a specialness in my mind. As the principal mosque in the capital, it was constantly teeming with people from all over the world. Each *Eid*, after returning from the mosque, we would accompany our mother to the neighbours' front-porch and give them a bowl of her sweet, milky *suveyas*. It was one of the few times that we saw our neighbours. They would chat with her at the door, discussing gardening and trivialities, lamenting about the lack of attendees at the local church.

'Nowadays,' they complained, 'only elderly folk attend the services. And, of course, those numbers are dwindling each year!' They added as a morbid afterthought.

They spoke of empty services across the country, and of vicars forced to make halls available for commercial purposes, and so when my mother described the crowds flocking to the mosque in the capital, they always seemed impressed.

'At least there,' the neighbours nodded, 'the space was being put to good use.'

Before we left, they handed her a leaflet with a programme of church services inviting her to come by sometime.

My mother was right though. Regent's Park Mosque seemed to heave with more and more people each year. On Friday afternoons especially, they would congregate from all four corners of the city. The women's section was a balconied area suspended above the men's section and each time the call to prayer sounded, I would peer down in between the banisters and watch the hall below surge with a sea of moving people. Up above, a huge crystal chandelier dangled from the centre of the golden, domed roof, dwarfing the procession below. It looked so heavy, I was constantly terrified that at any moment it might drop and crush the crowd prostrating below. Somebody told me it had been a gift from the King of Saudi Arabia and I remember thinking how much I wanted to visit this far-off place called

Saudi Arabia with its kind king. I think perhaps I imagined there would be golden domes everywhere and crystal chandeliers hanging from the skies.

But if the mosque was always packed, at the same time it was also a strange place filled with scores of strangers. Sometimes it seemed as if every language except English was spoken there. I would cling to my mother terrified we would become separated as we jostled from the ablution area to the women's section, stumbling through the huge pile of shoes left by the entrance. One time a girl pushed my sister, tripping her up, and I instinctively rushed to her aid. Although we were just small kids, Leila and I still managed to get in a scrum with the girl and her friends and, in the end, the *mosque-wallahs* had to break us all up. My mother chided us for the whole of the journey home. Afterwards, I learnt that the girl was the daughter of a *mullah*, and when Leila and I grew older, we joked that the incident summed up much of our relationship with religious orthodoxy.

At school, Leila and I were the only Muslims in our year. At the time, it was hard to work out what precisely that meant. For me, being Muslim simply meant a certain set of prohibitions. It meant I did not eat sausage rolls at lunch. It meant I did not play Spin-The-Bottle or kiss boys. And, above all, it meant I did not draw our creator, a lesson I had learnt somewhat belatedly after proudly exhibiting a cartoon character to my mother and explaining that Mrs. Brown had asked us to draw God. The smiling toothless stickman was promptly thrown into the bin. On Tuesday mornings, I would follow the rest of the children into Chapel for choir practice and sing the hymns just as vociferously as the chaplain, only ever catching my breath over the verses that referred to Christ as the son of God.

My best friend was the daughter of the French teacher. She hated choir practice. One morning on our way into Chapel, she declared with a hint of pride that she had turned 'ace-the-ist' and from then on during hymn practice, she would open and close her mouth like a fish so it looked as though she was singing but no noise would come out. Sometimes the teachers caught us whispering and they would eyeball us to return our concentration to the hymnals. We would quickly look down in unison and pretend to fumble with the pages. My best friend would resume her fish faces and I would return to the task of trying hard not to laugh.

Although religious education was a compulsory subject, the syllabus focused predominantly on Christianity. Most of the Jewish kids had letters of exemption from their parents and missed the classes but my parents gave me no such dispensation. While my friends hopscotched in the playground on extended breaks, I sat at the front of a classroom listening to the chaplain's lectures. I did not mind though, since I enjoyed the lessons. The chaplain was a kind, soft-spoken man and when he spoke of right and wrong, I could tell he was speaking from the heart. He quickly became my favourite teacher. Thanks to him I read most of the Bible before I read the *Quran*. I would listen intently during his classes, wholly absorbed by his words, taking notes and asking questions and at one point, I even committed to memory all the formalities for a church wedding. At home in the evenings, sometimes I sneaked down into the garage and tried on my mother's stilettos as I practised the lines to myself, wondering whether I would have to repeat them some day at a similar ceremony when I grew up.

When it came to learning about world religions, the chaplain organised a minibus and visits to a synagogue and a gurudwara. But at the gurudwara, I was shocked when I saw him kneel and kiss the Sikh holy book by way of example to the rest of the class. My mother had taught me only to kneel before God and so I hung back and avoided the ritual, although it felt awkward at the time and I tried to compensate by over-thanking the priest when he ladled out sweet *prasad* into my hands just before we left. It felt rude not being able to explain. Later that evening, when I told my mother about the delicious sweet-dish distributed at the temple, she smiled and explained that the reason it tasted so good was because it had been blessed.

The chaplain told me that one day he would organise a trip to a mosque too. I guess he never got around to it though for I never visited a mosque with my school.

During a couple of lessons, the chaplain touched briefly on Islam and each time he looked to me to crosscheck things as he flicked through the pages of our textbook. Whenever he did, I grew self-conscious. No one seemed to know much about my religion back then, not even the chaplain in spite of his curiosity. As for my class fellows, they seemed more distracted by the pictures in their books. One of the pages contained a photograph of a bride wearing a heavily adorned outfit, dripping with gold just like the ones I had seen in Kashmir when I was a child. A veil covered her head, and her hands and feet were stained with patterns made from dark-red henna. The girls in my class had never seen anything like it and asked me if I would be getting married in the same style. My face burned beetroot with embarrassment. At the request of the chaplain, I brought in prayer-mats and headscarves and a copy of the *Quran* from home. The chaplain asked me questions and each time I tried to answer as best as I could, but sometimes I stuttered through my explanations with difficulty or without understanding. It bothered me that I could not answer properly. When I went home, I asked my mother to explain things to me. At one point I started to feel myself becoming an ambassador of something much greater, something ungraspable, and with that, a part of me began to feel woefully inadequate. In those moments, it was as if a guilt leaked out from somewhere deep inside and made me feel like a fraud.

For the most part, school was a time of uncovering secret

passageways and opening gigantic wooden doors. I was tipped into the wider world slowly and asked to find my way, just like the adventures of The Lion, the Witch and the Wardrobe, The Wizard of Oz, Watership Down and The Labyrinth. After all, what were those tales but paradigms of the extraordinary journeys I was making?

At first, it began with just the small things, like the trade of stickers that took place in the school playground, when huddles of children would barter for a 'shiny' or a 'furry' or a particularly rare sticker that came from some far flung spot in the world. Pupils would return from holidays boasting unique purchases and chatting excitedly about foreign places filled with magic art shops spilling with coloured tissue paper, ultraviolet pens and tubes of glittery stars. I longed to visit them. I wanted to go to Disney Land, to Florida, Sydney, Paris, Egypt, Rome and China. Instead, I began collecting their artefacts. To my delight, I discovered a fortuitous knack for bargaining and by the end of the year, I succeeded in growing the largest sticker collection in my class, full of dancing cartoon characters, hieroglyphic symbols and sparkling Matryoshka dolls.

As I coloured in maps during our geography classes, I learnt about the countries where my stickers came from, the seven floating continents and how the earth was broken into blocks, not whole as I once imagined. My stickers hailed from places as far off as Japan, Russia and Africa, and I grew very attached to my collection, perhaps a little too attached. Every evening I flicked through the album with Leila admiring the latest additions, proudly describing where each sticker came from and its relative worth until, one day, out of the blue, my mother gave my album away. I was angry and hurt when I found out. My mother told me she had given the album to our cleaner's niece who was visiting from Jamaica. For some strange reason, this thought consoled me. I suppose I imagined my album being shown off in some exotic, far off place and the idea made me a little happier. In the mailbox at the top of our hill, I posted a letter to the girl enclosing a few more stickers.

Back in the playground, I moved on to new trades and new merchandise, bartering marbles and stamps for small change. As soon as I scrounged enough pennies, I would dash to the tuckshop and buy as many marshmallows as I could. One pence, two pence, five pence … I would count the copper coins ever so slowly, pushing them across the counter one by one, while the tuckshop lady looked on, frowning impatiently.

And then, at a certain point, our white-haired neighbourhood changed. It happened so quickly, as if overnight. I woke to discover all the elderly, retired folk gone and a wave of teenagers in their place. The area began to fill with a new kind of energy. An electric sort of energy. I started noticing things. Images on television. Sound-bites on the radio. Advertisement boards. Headlines in the newspapers. A man came to our house and installed a special modem giving us instant World Wide Web access.

'The first of its kind,' he said.

A ringtone sounded and the cheerful chirping of a bird signalled that the connection had been established. At school, our history teacher bombarded us with fact after fact, booming out a multitude of names, dates and events as if a microphone was attached to his lapel. All at once, I was hit with a volley of sensations and impressions. Bits of information came flying at me. The Magna Carta, the Bayeux Tapestry, 1066, Marconi and the radio waves, Samuel Morse and his code, the Wright brothers and their flying machine, NASA, space. Things started travelling and sticking, they started to join and connect like the spaghetti alphabet hoops floating in my tomato sauce at lunchtime that I scooped up with my fork.

French classes began and the French teacher walked up and down the aisle in the room chanting 'Alhoetta', smelling of cigarettes and stale coffee. Each time she passed, I rolled my tongue and chanted the rhyme back. I learnt about the rise and fall of distant empires, absent civilisations and disappeared peoples: the Aztecs and the Mayans, the Vikings and the Anglo-Saxons, the Tudors, the Ancient Greeks and the Romans. One afternoon, a band of actors came to perform sections of The Odyssey and I watched my classics teacher clap enthusiastically as a brawny-looking Odysseus met famous dead people in the Underworld, entirely oblivious to the boys sniggering at the front of the class. The school bus ferried me between different realms like Charon's boat. I became an explorer, going deeper into the forest with my pencil and notebook, collecting oak leaves and conkers and mapping out my own ecosystem onto the earth with a ruler and compass. I buried acorns in the soil, like a squirrel readying for winter, entrusting the land with my treasure. I visited ruins and old monuments. I learnt about times I did not know, places I had not been and histories that were not my own. There was so much to learn, so many dates and numbers and words. But sometimes it was all too much and there were moments I struggled to grapple the things being put before me, like why an atomic bomb had been dropped on Nagasaki even after the horror of Hiroshoma, or how a mad scientist had been allowed to conduct Frankenstein-like experiments on twins in the crazed belief of creating a super-race. At one point, I remember standing on a vast green field looking out at a dizzying line of white plaques stretching across the rolling countryside, feeling utterly overwhelmed.

Our teacher read out loud in slow solemnity, 'We are the dead.'

Though I did not understand all of what he said, the sadness of those four words struck me somewhere deep inside.

Hitting thirteen became an existential nightmare. I was a late developer and all sorts of strange things started happening to my body. All of a sudden bits started appearing from nowhere. At the school canteen, I got up from my chair and realised with panic, that it was me and not the bolognese that had stained my seat crimson. My body underwent a strange physical metamorphosis. In its new form, I found I could no longer go jogging in my shorts without attracting a chorus of honks from passing cars. Even running on the tennis court began to feel clunky, and it felt even worse at the tennis centre.

After school, my father would collect us and drive to the local tennis centre, dropping us off and leaving us to our own devices until late in the evenings when he returned to pick us up on his way back from work. The centre was an enormous complex, with fifteen indoor Plexipave tennis courts, eight badminton courts and twelve outdoor hard courts. From one side of the centre, a viewing gallery on the first floor looked out onto the courts below, and behind the gallery a bar area served chocolate bars and microwavable pub food like shepherds pie or lasagne. On the ground level, to one side of the reception, there was a gym and fitness studio. As we started growing older, we trained later. Courts could be booked up to eleven o'clock at night. Before, playing tennis in skirts and vest-tops had been routine. But now Leila would become embarrassed whenever boys came over to watch. In the evenings especially, a group of teenagers would lean over the side of the viewing gallery, clapping and wolf-whistling. There would always be a crowd. Still, my father insisted on booking the show-court to make us grow accustomed to playing before an audience. He disapproved of us wearing jumpers and jogging bottoms.

'No pyjamas!' he would shout.

Such things were an impediment to exercise, a sign of lethargy. And so, despite our natural shyness, we would always play in skirts. Eventually, I suppose, we grew used to it.

But it was at the tennis centre that I started to see all sorts of things. Things that I saw for the first time. Things that intrigued me. Things that startled me. Things that made me want to know more. The centre attracted a melting pot of people from

42

all across the city. So many passed through its doors. At different times, different people came. I learnt to recognise their comings and goings.

In the early mornings the runners came wearing leg supports and sweat bands. Some would use the bicycle stands at the front to stretch and do warm up exercises. As the day continued, they were followed by the more senior players who came for a few sets of mixed doubles before heading off for a boozy lunch in the bar. By midday, the school buses pulled up and half a dozen courts would be swarmed by unenthusiastic, slightly chubby-looking kids. The coaches fed them buckets of balls, making them run in exasperation from one side of the court to the other. By the end of the session, there were always considerably fewer balls in the buckets and the coaches would be left scratching their heads. By the late afternoons, an entourage of fancy cars took over the car park and I came to recognise the suave veneer of the city professionals. They were fashionable, athletic types and always wore expensive sportswear, heading straight to the gym to sweat, swear and grunt in the weights-room, surgically attached to their headsets and music players. After school, a gaggle of teenagers would slink in as the kickboxing and karate classes began. The skinny Asian kids always opted for badminton practice.

At the first sign of light fading, more cars screeched their way in playing loud electronic music, and the bar behind the club filled up. By evening, another wave of gym-goers arrived, heading straight into aerobic classes. Each time the door swung open I heard the punchy sound of the stereo pumping motivational beats. But the evening also signalled tennis lessons for the bored house-wives whose husbands worked late or were away on business. Their lessons always seemed something of a masquerade. Middle-aged women flirted provocatively with their considerably younger coaches. They wore full make-up and waved their long garish-coloured nails through the air. Their coaches stood tantalisingly close, pressing from behind, with toothpaste-advert smiles, gripping their student's racquets and mimicking the motions of forehand and backhand strokes. A pungent stench of perfume and aftershave lingered long after the sessions making me crease up my nose. In the changing-rooms, I would shower and sometimes catch the reflection of the other women in the mirror, quietly comparing my body to theirs and longing to possess the smooth curve of womanhood that ran down their backs. Their shapes always looked so much more refined than mine.

On the weekends, the centre was packed with a jumble of all sorts, and it became a cacophony of shouting, screaming, barking, squealing kids and adults alike. The chaos continued all weekend until the clock struck eleven on Sunday night and the players cleared from the courts. As activity gravitated towards the bar, the courts grew depressingly quiet. We would still be practising our drills when the lights above automatically flickered on and off in warning before the entire playing area descended into darkness.

After our practice sessions, Leila and I waited by the glass doors at the reception watching people enter and exit. My gaze would follow strangers' footsteps to the carpark in curiosity. If the centre gestured towards the greater, larger world that lay beyond, then at the same time, those swinging glass doors were always a reminder that it was a stopping point only, like a transit lounge that forever held me at bay. Eventually, the sight of my father's car would pull into view and the sound of an impatient car horn would start, cutting my reveries short. Each time I heard the blasts, I jumped up like a robot and ran out, pulled back once more into the sanctuary of the close and familiar.

Back at school, with each month that passed, kilts rolled up higher and the heels of our shoes grew narrower and taller. Hair was highlighted and collars raised as top buttons loosened. The girls scrawled lyrics and love-hearts into their notebooks. My best friend and I snuck into the local cinema, underage, and giggled at the nude scenes. I began to read silly teenage romances and followed soap operas about dysfunctional Australian families halfway across the world. It was like dominos as one by one everybody started to fall in and out of love. The boys drooled over the English teacher as she crooned out Keatsian odes, and the girls swooned over the boys in turn. I was no different. For several months, a plucky, red-haired boy who sat opposite me in my French class made my life sweet misery. Each time I saw him, I thought of French kisses and a bout of butterflies would release in my belly, but I was too shy to tell him. In the mornings, I looked forward to the classes we shared together. During the lessons, my gaze would stray his way guiltily and it did not take long before Leila picked up on my thoughts, and in no time at all everybody at home came to know. My sister teased me when I received my first Valentine's Day card and I squirmed in discomfort as the colours of feeling passed through my face like a slideshow. 'Be my Valentine', the card read with a smattering of kisses. No signature. It was anonymous. I buried the card beneath my pillow, digging it out each night to re-read with a little guilt.

In the common rooms, teenage magazines were strewn about carelessly and girls chatted about the agony aunt pages and joked about their latest exploits in internet chat-rooms and on sex education phone-lines. During the breaks we sometimes dialled free-phone numbers from the school payphone and invented imaginary problems. My friends would conjure all sorts of elaborate complications but my attempts were meek, and it would not be long before I hung up with embarrassment. One day a pupil turned up to school completely tangerine in colour looking like she had just been Tango'd like the orange man in the television ad and our teacher could not hide his smiles. The pupil tried to shrug off the stares, boasting that she had just come back from the Caribbean, but we all knew it was a spray-tan gone wrong. Girls pointed out the tell-tale signs of self-tanning, like

45

the pale skin between the fingers or the white patches behind the ear lobes. One of the girls had her bellybutton pierced and came into school sporting a flesh-tight shirt and a crystal stud hanging in her navel. She boasted how much her boyfriend loved it. We gathered round enthusiastically, studying the hole, eager to know how much it had hurt.

At fourteen, I got my first mobile phone. It looked like a walkie-talkie. I swapped numbers with my friends and played the free ringtones on repeat. At about the same time, I started experimenting with make-up. The first time was a special day. I had spent several months collecting foundation bottles, mascara, eye-liner, blushers, combs, lip-sticks, glosses and all sorts of other items in preparation for the occasion, even pinching a few make-up brushes from my mother's cosmetics box. On the evening before my fourteenth birthday, I sat before the mirror surveying my face like it was a blank canvass, trying hard to recall the way my mother applied the moisturising cream to her face. Her dressing table always seemed like a small shrine when I was young, scattered with candles, papier-mâché jewellery boxes and perfume pots. I used to sit on the carpet beside her, watching the powdery show unravel. If I was lucky, sometimes I would receive a squirt of scent or a stroke of nail-varnish.

Sitting there in front of that mirror for the first time with all those tools around me, suddenly felt exciting. I dabbed my face with foundation, rubbing it into my skin in circular motions just like my mother did. Not really knowing what to do next, I picked up a bottle of mascara and used the brush to trace my eyelashes until they were long and jet black. Next, I took out a charcoal eyeliner and applied the pencil to the under-rims of my eyes. I had seen many of the older girls do it in the same way in the mirrors in the school toilets. Then I drew two half-moons over my cheeks with a large, bristly blusher-brush. I was almost done. I took out a lipstick and rolled the rose tint over my lips, pressing them together and finishing off my pout with a soft, peachy gloss. When I stepped back from the mirror, I barely recognised myself. I felt utterly transformed. I had created something new, something different, something with … green eyes. It was the first time I noticed my eyes. They were foreign-looking.

That night, I went out clubbing in central London for the first time. Going out underage was a rite of passage. Limelights. I can still remember the club's name. My best friend and I had spent the whole week fretting about what to wear and which night-buses we would take home. The venue was dark and full of serpentine corridors and within minutes of entering, I lost sight of my friend. She resurfaced attached at the mouth to someone who looked three times her age. Everything seemed to gravitate towards a heavy pulsating mass at the end of one room. I remember swaying through bodies as if in some dream. Wave upon wave of dark bodies. Bodies on the floor. Bodies on the stairwells. Bodies tucked away in corners and alcoves. They seemed to lean in towards me. I spent half the night pushing away wandering hands and limbs, thinking my father had probably been right to disapprove of me going to such places.

'You don't drink?' a boy in a half-open shirt scoffed at the bar.

It was a question that with time, increased in frequency, and I never knew how to answer. I did not drink, but I was not sure why. After all, my father drank. I made excuses to my friends. But as alcohol seeped into their world, I found myself becoming estranged from them. They spent their evenings loitering in the park drinking from bottles and mixing tonics. It would always end the same way, violently sick and passing out over one another, only to wake the following morning with pounding headaches and yet somehow convinced they had just had the best night of the year. I never understood it. On Friday nights, most of the school descended on a local pub and played drinking games late into the night. I lacked the same enthusiasm.

It always struck me as a medieval-looking watering hole full of slightly balding, slightly lecherous middle-aged men. Perhaps you needed to drink to move past the disappointment, but I never drank. Once I took a sip out of curiosity and immediately felt ashamed. The taste soured the insides of my mouth. After that, I promised myself that I would never do it again. Perhaps then, a part of me began to feel secretly relieved when my growing engagement with tennis meant I did not have to spend my Friday nights in the local pub wrestling with the rationale behind my Diet Coke.

What began at the back of our garden with my sister in Alderton Hill, moved on to club ladders at the tennis centre, slowly progressing into county-level matches and national competitions, before eventually graduating to international tournaments. As our engagement with tennis grew, Leila and I would often leave home on Friday evenings to drive out to different parts of England for a never-ending sequence of weekend tournaments.

Without fully realising it, I passed through so much of England this way: Corby, Felixstowe, Frinton, Winchester, Hertfordshire, Cardiff, Bath, Telford, Nottingham ... so many other English cities that I may not have otherwise seen. We would leave straight after school, only stopping by our home to collect our bags and racquets. It would always be dark by the time my father began the drive and we would curl up under blankets in the back. I grew to love those long journeys on the road. Rural England was truly beautiful. At night, the countryside opened up like a carpet of darkening shades and textures and I would drift in and out of consciousness watching the steady stretch of dimly-lit motorway contour through flat and sloping landscapes. Through half-closed eyes, sometimes I saw the tiny white stars peeping down at me.

Tennis took me beyond the parochial limits of Alderton Hill and released me into a vast new world. It was a varied, hungry and irrepressible world and each day I saw more of it. I played on public hard courts in parks surrounded by council estates where the local kids came out to watch. I saw families arguing, couples swearing at one another, two men kissing. I played on Astro Turf in the middle of isolated industrial sites and army bases in the pouring rain. At night, my sister and I shared rooms in hotels and chuckled at the strange noises coming through the walls. In suburban sports complexes, gangs of youths smoked outside by the bins and intentionally caused havoc for the police. I kept my head down and played on, serving and swinging until eventually I carried my racquets onto the courts of some the country's most prestigious clubs, where ladies in aprons cut fat slices of cake and piled my plate high with scones and cream. At the end of my match, an attendant in the dressing room handed me a thick towel and offered to pour my bath as I peeled off my sweaty clothes.

Moving on to junior international tournaments, I met people from all over the world. Some of the Russian girls had surnames that were even longer than my own. I learnt how to curse in a dozen languages. I learnt about apartheid from a South African player. I played cards with an Egyptian girl who refused to compete against an Israeli player, and through that exchange I learnt about Palestine. A parent made a disparaging remark about an Iraqi girl with the surname Hussein, and from that careless aside, I was introduced to the Gulf War. Suddenly, school life and the Friday night excesses seemed so small. I was meeting people from all walks of life and was curious to know more about the lives and places they came from. And of course, seeing my unusual name, it was only a matter of time before they became curious to know the same about me.

But at some level, I was struggling to find myself. Beneath the surface, there were times when I felt completely lost inside and I did not know who I was. In the evenings, when I went home, I showered and washed my face, scrubbing away make-up. Sometimes afterwards, I stood in front of the mirror, naked, and saw a pale-skinned girl staring back with sharp, angular features and strange green eyes. I got on with everybody, but felt like nobody. I felt it most when I was alone on those long contemplative journeys on the road. Sometimes, it would rain. The rain would trickle down the window panes and make all sorts of wonderful shapes in the wind and I would see the world reflected back to me in strange and startling ways through the droplets. As the water quivered and gave way, the patterns changed. New drops formed and the process would start again. I would watch the changing patterns in silence for hours, wondering why anyone needed to go to a house of prayer when I could feel so at peace just by watching the rain.

Other realisations were happening more slowly. I remember the first time my coach mimicked my father in a thick foreign accent. I smiled in confusion although the joke had surely hurt. I did not think my father spoke in that way. But that evening, at the dining table, I listened carefully. It was the first time I noticed he had a slight accent.

It had been almost a decade since I had visited Kashmir. During that time, I came to know that an armed insurgency had amassed across the Valley, though I knew very little about it or the sequence of events that led to that movement. Some of my cousins who lived through the turmoil later spoke of 'being part of history', but I never really understood what they meant. All I knew was that the Valley was no longer a safe place to go.

Very little news filtered back from that place. At times when we were eating together, I heard my father shouting down a crackly telephone line in Kashmiri. He would motion to Leila and I to stop chatting while he spoke loudly down the receiver, and for a few moments the whole dining table would fall silent. But even those calls were rare. It was always difficult to get through from London. My parents spoke to one another afterwards, mixing their conversation in different languages. Perhaps they thought Leila and I would not understand, but although they had not taught us Kashmiri, my father had a habit of scolding us in his native tongue and over time, I learnt to pick up bits and was able to stitch their conversations together backwards. Through the years, I followed various stories in this way. Stories of soldiers coming to search homes in the middle of the night. Stories of makeshift interrogation cells set up in hotels. One had been set up next to my uncle's house and he would hear screams coming from it throughout the night. Boys had gone missing. Parents were desperate to send their kids abroad. Households that had never before left the Valley were pleading for their sons to work elsewhere. A bride had been raped on her wedding day. My cousin, Farrah, had left with her family. Their servant turned up at the house one day with guns and men and demanded that she marry him. My uncle had reassured them that she would be married in the morning, but as soon as the men left, he gathered the family and fled. They left everything behind. I never knew what happened to Farah. Perhaps she was in America now. The last time I saw her, I had been a toddler and she drew a pencil sketch for me. I remember that picture. I had watched mesmerised as the strokes and lines came together to trace the outlines of a woman with beautiful, long voluminous hair looking out from a window. She had signed the drawing for me and I was convinced that one day she would become a famous painter.

Although there were several relatives on my mother's side scattered about the country, we had no real Kashmiri community in England. At some stage a vague association had been set up and it held sporadic meetings in the North. Most of the gatherings were fundraisers and we travelled up from London. Some of the uncles from the association had also gathered outside Downing Street with my mother in a small picket, holding banners and chanting slogans. Leila and I were young at the time and they gave us placards and marker pens to keep us preoccupied. We sat together on the pavement colouring the signs with black and red ink. It had been a cold day, but it felt warm being in a huddle. A man with a microphone came to Leila and asked why we were there.

'Because our mama is here,' she told him.

It was true. At that time I did not understand the slogans. I did not know the faces of the boys in the posters. I did not know who their parents were or what homes they came from. They just looked like other children.

After a while, the fundraisers petered out and slowly those uncles faded from my life. My mother stopped going into the streets and holding banners outside Downing Street. The association fragmented. At one of the last fundraisers the organisers arranged a quiz with questions on Kashmir for the kids. Like Leila and I, many of the children had only visited the Valley as toddlers before the troubles began. Kashmir had been largely inaccessible for most of our adolescent years, and the whole landscape of the Valley was so far removed from our reality that completing the quiz was virtually impossible. Eventually, the organisers were forced to hand out the answer-sheets. Bit by bit, families stopped driving up for the meetings and the association grew defunct. In the end, I only saw the other children at the occasional wedding.

After that, the only news that came from the Valley was drip-fed through those irregular phone calls at the dining table. People would ring from Kashmir and ask my father to look after their sons or nephews who had come to work in England. My father often sponsored young Kashmiri students and sometimes they would come around for dinner. Most of them rented accommodation in East Ham and would tell many sad and varied stories of immigrant life. One time, four boys came over and told us they were sharing a single-room studio flat in Upton Park. An opportunist landlord was charging them £400 a week and they had been forced to take out loans. The local gurdwara distributed free *prasad* in the mornings and they would eat there once a week to avoid spending money. Although they were Muslim, the boys had been welcomed. Whenever they came over, my mother cooked Kashmiri food and they would be reminded of home.

But at that time, everything that came from the Valley was foreign and unrecognisable to me, even the people that passed through our home. I struggled to identify with them and perhaps deep down there was a part of me that did not want to. They represented something I did not understand, something that had been usurped and was no longer a part of my reality: the accents, the clothes, the music, the cheesy new Bollywood flicks with their spandex heroes and lycra heroines gyrating against a backdrop of modern flashing European cities. Everything that now came from that part of the world was alien to me. I grew up barely conscious that I had a homeland. There was a place I visited long ago. There were people I had known. But that special place was somewhere else now. Those people I had known were no longer here. I had been too young to understand it properly. Somehow time got lost in imagination. Whatever Kashmir was, it became just a fond memory, a story. Even my father's parents, they had not died, they had simply disappeared. As time passed, even their stories were fading. I was forgetting everything about them. There was nothing to keep them alive except for a few old photo-frames. I could hardly remember them. There was once a world, I thought, or had it all been just a dream?

One late afternoon in the autumn, Leila and I were playing tennis at the back of our garden in Alderton Hill. I was sweeping the leaves off the court like I always did at the start of our practice. Pinkish-red and orange clusters had gathered in small heaps on the acrylic surface. Some were picked up and dragged away in the wind. Some were still dancing, twirling in tantric circles until they were blown against the wire netting.

Somewhere in the distance, someone was burning leaves. Maybe it was an early bonfire. Maybe someone was lighting firecrackers. I stopped in my tracks as all of a sudden an inexplicable smell filled my nostrils. It must have lasted only a couple of seconds before a gust of wind snatched it away. But it was undeniable. It was the smell of the White House.

In all my life, I have never come across such a potent sense of something so familiar and yet so vast, so utterly incomprehensible. The smell tore through my heart, shaking the cinders of something buried deep inside. I breathed in the air intensely and for a moment I fancied that perhaps the breeze responded to my recognition, lingering about my face caressing me softly like a shawl, before tearing itself away and vanishing. Something, some sacred memory, departed with that sense of smell that left me all of a sudden beggared and nursing an unbearable sense of loss. It was in that moment I realised I had lost something. I had lost something special, something fiercely precious. Only, what that something was, eluded me. It eluded me even before I had the chance to fully comprehend it. For several minutes, I stood there waiting for the smell to return. After a while, I began chasing after the wind in vain. The light started to fade from the sky, but the smell never came back. I watched the autumn leaves break off and fall around me and I suddenly felt like crying. Sometimes, even now, a part of me still wonders … do even the smells of a place flee in the wake of war?

I did not know much about the events that led to Ami and Papa coming to England. In all Papa's stories, he never really spoke of that time or how he came to be separated from the Valley. All I knew was that my mother was born during the period my grandparents were in Pakistan and she had spent her early years growing up in a small village outside one of the major trading towns, not far from the capital, Islamabad. My mother rarely spoke of her early childhood, and for a long time I imagined that perhaps the memories of those initial years had strayed into some irretrievable place, forgotten. But for that brief accidental spell, it might as well have been that Pakistan never really happened and my mother spent all her formative years growing up in England. So it was with some surprise that one afternoon I realised I had in fact been mistaken all along. We were walking down the local high street when something in a shop window caught her eye. It was a small porcelain doll dressed in a blue cotton frock. My mother stared at it for some time without saying a word before turning to me and explaining it reminded her of Pakistan. And I guess that was how it unfolded.

In Pakistan, my mother grew up on the bottom floor of a three-storey communal block which looked out onto a small courtyard. The home was compact and unadorned, a modest dwelling for a young family. Only one person could enter the kitchen at any given time, and it was usually Ami, my grandmother, who monopolised that space. A mixing bowl of people lived in the courtyard. Among them, a family of soap-makers with four young children who lived on the bottom floor, and next to them an elderly carpenter and his wife. Later on, a few other Kashmiri families moved into the block, including two handsome brothers. The brothers were of marriageable age and caused quite a stir when they first arrived, setting off a string of Chinese whispers amongst the neighbours. It was not long before all the children on the block knew about them and were convinced that the Central Intelligence Department had come to spy on their activities. In the afternoons, they played hide and seek around the courtyard, murmuring the latest sightings of secret agents. My mother would join in too, looking out over the turrets and rooftops and poking her head around street corners trying to keep an eye on strangers idly hanging around the building. And maybe, to their credit, given the nature of those times, there was something in it that was more than make-believe.

But for the most part, during those fledgling years in Pakistan, my mother lived a carefree and haphazard existence, caught up in a world of fiction and fable, too preoccupied enacting her own adventures around the courtyard with the other children to notice the small daily struggles of Ami and Papa. Each morning, she would travel to school by *tanga* beside the *tanga-wallah*, sitting behind a great white stallion while her best-friend ran alongside the horse. Her friend loved to run, refusing to take a lift in the horse cart. Her long jet-black hair would stream out just like the horse's tail as she raced along and from the top of the carriage my mother would watch with an inkling of envy, wishing her own curls were as silky and straight.

For my mother, Pakistan meant making dams and rivulets in the mud so that the water collected in little estuaries and artificial pools in the centre of the courtyard. It meant going to see a black and white movie, *Nagin*, about two children who turned into snakes, while she shovelled popcorn into her mouth and tapped her foot along to the songs. It meant trundling along with Papa to the army base and riding inside a tank with a tall moustachioed man. One time, they travelled late at night in the pitch-black darkness in the back of an open truck and heard wolves howling in the wilderness. The next morning, a man with an orange beard showed her leopard cubs and she played with them on his front lawn.

Pakistan meant picking small chillies from the chilli bush, wrapping them inside grape vine and eating them like *paan*. The first time the other children showed her how, she had felt all grown-up. It meant reddish-orange maltas leaking out a blood-coloured juice when you cut them open, and fuzzy, round peaches like the ones she gave me on my first day at school. My mother had never eaten a peach before and hoarded it as if it was the most precious thing she owned. Only after everybody else had finished eating theirs did she dig her own out carefully and cut it into eight equal pieces to share amongst her siblings. When the summer heat beat down, smothering the city in a smog of humidity and making the thermostats rocket, she and her siblings would pull the mattresses from their beds and take them up onto the roof to sleep outside in the open. Sometimes it rained in the middle of the night and she would stumble through the puddles, dragging her mattress back down again, sleepy-eyed and sodden.

One day, out of the blue, one of the handsome Kashmiri brothers gave her a beautiful blue clockwork doll. The doll could walk when it was wound up and my mother immediately fell in love with it, caring for it like it was her own child. She was playing with that doll on the day Ami called her into the courtyard, and along with the rest of the family, she lined up as a man with a trim moustache and a red pocket square took a photograph of them all in front of their home. It was the last photograph taken of their life in Pakistan. That afternoon, bags were assembled and she was ushered into a jeep. The two handsome brothers helped Papa carry the luggage into the car. Among the suitcases, there were big tins and bedding rolled up and tied together with leather bands. In the rush, my mother's clockwork doll was forgotten. By the time she realised, it was too late. The bags were filled, and already stacked into the car. Ami told her to give the doll to one of the soap-maker's children. My mother did so, obediently, but big salty tears rolled down her cheeks as they drove away. As she told me the story of that beloved blue doll, I could not help thinking back to my old sticker album. A sudden twinge of regret overcame me as I wondered where it was in the world.

On 3 November 1959, my mother's family left Pakistan on a PIA flight to London Heathrow. At the entrance of the plane, two air-hostesses wearing beige uniforms designed by Yves Saint Laurent greeted them with sparkling Colgate smiles. There were no other children on the flight apart from my mother and her brothers. Most of the passengers were young men and the air-hostesses were sympathetic, even taking my mother into the cockpit to watch how the plane was piloted as it landed into Heathrow. She would never forget it. Her first memory of England was peering out of the window from the cockpit as the plane glided down over the city and seeing hundreds of thousands of little lights twinkling in the darkness below.

'It was the same memory,' my mother said, 'that came back fifty years later, the first time I looked out across the Thames at night from the penthouse', when she and my father stepped out onto the terrace of their new home and saw the mass of lights sprinkled like fire-flies opening up before them.

I often try to imagine what it must have been like for my mother coming to a new country for the first time. I struggle to picture her growing up in the North of England. In my head, I have this snapshot of her transformed to that slightly dirty greyish colour people from hot countries go when suddenly placed in colder climates. I see her standing in a roll call with her siblings all duffle-coated up wearing strange, outdated clothes on a cloudy November morning. She is standing there long-plaited, and underneath her coat I see her dressed to the eyeballs in her best clothes. A turquoise *shalwar kameez* spattered with sequins and mirror-work peeps from the hem. I think of her peering from the glass panes as the train chugs along northwards, and being struck by the sight of women working in shop windows. I see the two large water-work chimneys standing at the gateway of the industrial city that would go on to become her home. I think of her competing with her siblings to press the buttons in the lift of their council flat, experimenting with the numbers each time they pinged the shaft up and down. That first night in England when there were so many loud bangs and explosions outside, and they had all grown frightened, not knowing it was the 5th of November, not knowing anything at all about Guy Fawkes.

Sometimes I try hard to think what it must have been

like. I try my best to understand. I picture the long balconies and Papa's little Kashmiri papier-mâché bell ornament on the mantelpiece by the gas fireplace. I think of my mother doing mundane things like going to school and her first day when all the girls had gathered around asking if they could be her friend, or the time when one of the teachers made her stand up in class and point to where she came from on the map. I think of her playing hockey, reading Bunty comics and setting the dining table with forks and knives. The first time she ate Hovis bread with butter and jam and how she and her brothers sat at the table and finished several loaves in one go. The broken farmer slogans that were merrily bandied about those days: 'Drink-a-pint-a-milk-a-day!' and 'Go to work on an egg!' The argument she had with her siblings at their first Christmas over whether the song was Jingo bells or Jingle bells, and the girl next-door who walked back home with her after school wearing an ice-skating tutu and smelling of a strange heavy odour, the same smell that came with her menstruation cycle.

I try to imagine the December morning when Papa returned from work with a car and how the whole family celebrated, with Ami cooking her special *tabak-maaz*. I see my mother sitting lovingly by the wheels, one by one taking out the stones from the grooves so that they stayed in pristine condition. And the following weekend, when Papa drove them all into Piccadilly Circus to see the Christmas lights, how the beacons of colour shone back in the glass windows multiplied ten-fold like a fairground! I picture my mother growing up slowly. I see her being summoned to the front of the school assembly with the naughtiest boy in her class while her favourite teacher looked on sorrowfully.

'From now on,' the headmistress reprimanded, 'you must speak *only* English.'

And so, bit by bit, my mother forgot the language she had learnt in Pakistan.

I see a miniature version of her pottering around in Manchester with a Mancunian accent and picture the small park where she went to feed the ducks. Once, at the small park, she got into a fight with a boy when her younger brother cried for help.

'*Bhaji, Bhaji*! My nose! My nose!' he sobbed.

His glasses were shattered and his nose bloodied. An older boy stood over him, laughing.

'Go home Paki!'

My mother rushed over immediately, pushing the boy away, but he yanked hard on her hair, and that evening, when she combed it, large clumps fell out.

Sometimes after school, my mother would go to her best friend's house for egg and chips, and other times Gladys would come to my mother's home for curry and rice. In the evenings, she would stitch her dresses in her bedroom. As time passed, the colour choices brightened, the cuts became a little more daring, the sleeves a little shorter, although never too obvious to be picked up by the warden-like eye of Ami. At sixteen, the hairdresser cut off my mother's plaits, leaving her with a bed of short, stylish curls and on Friday nights, Gladys would come knocking on the door to try to persuade Ami to let her go to the local disco. But, back then, my grandmother was not the soft, pliable Ami that I knew and loved, and she would stand at the door cross-armed and stern like an eagle. Even so, sometimes my mother would hover in the hallway, wearing a little mascara, just in case.

My mother had an arranged marriage. A family friend from Kashmir proposed the match when he came to know that my father had recently moved to England as a young medical graduate. The wedding was a modest celebration and took place in a small community hall in Manchester. Ami did the cooking.

On our long walk together, I found out that my mother kept a diary when she was young. After she married, she had locked it away in the bank along with her most precious jewellery. Until then, she had never mentioned it to me, but sometimes I wonder what is written in it. I wondered whether perhaps my mother's stories would fill the gaps in mine. Somewhere out there with all her wedding gold, the rest of those stories were gathering dust, buried away in a vault that I could never open.

After their wedding, my parents moved into a studio flat in the south of London. They were given a large woollen Kashmiri carpet to take with them, but the flat was small and over-cramped and there was no floor-space to roll it out. In the end, they had to keep it bound up in one corner. A worn chest of drawers helped prop it up. On all sides of the room, the walls were made of brick. An industrial-looking metal sink jutted out from one edge, barely a metre away from the foot of a small sofa-bed. My parents spent their first night together here. Many years later, my mother told me she had only ever seen my father cry twice. The first time was on their wedding night. You see, none of his family had been able to come from Kashmir for the marriage ceremony.

After the summer vacations were over, I joined the Sixth Form. Some of my class-fellows left and a new batch of students arrived, among them, a large number of Asian kids. Most of the new joiners were of Indian origin, but a few were of Pakistani descent. In some strange turn of coincidence, at about the same time, several Asian families moved into our neighbourhood.

For many years, we had been the only Asian family on Alderton Hill. Our neighbours were retired and elderly, and gradually over the years the two couples that lived on either side of us became two singles. For the most part they kept to themselves and, except for those *Eid* visitations, I rarely saw them. Sometimes, but only very rarely, my sister and I were forced to creep under the holes in the hedgerows and sneak into their gardens to retrieve our missing tennis balls. Each ball could cost up to a pound of our pocket-money. We would take it in turns to push each other through the thickets, yelping when the twigs and branches caught on clothing and scratched our legs. Across on the other side, the gardens were still and quiet. Once I caught sight of a fox skulking past the back fence but that was the only movement I ever saw on those lawns. The houses stood aloof as if uninhabited for many years. I would see our tennis balls standing out like pots of gold in the greenery and quickly dash over to collect them, then sprint back to the cover of the bushes while my sister stood guard by the opening, keeping watch to make sure I could always return. And so, the first time my mother told me that one of our neighbours had sold his home and that a young Asian family was moving in, the news came as a great surprise.

As soon as I heard the sound of a car pulling into the driveway and the voices of children, I rushed to the window to catch a glimpse of our new neighbours. They were a Sikh family; a middle-aged couple with two girls roughly my own age, and a boy. My parents went across to welcome them and it was not long before Leila and I were called forward to greet them too. We wandered across shyly, smiling politely. A couple of months later, their son got married and we all watched open-mouthed as a white stallion, garlanded from head to toe in carnations, emerged from out of nowhere on our hill and crossed over to their front drive. All the other neighbours must have been watching from their windows too. All the way up the hill, I was sure the curtains were drawn, with noses pressed against the windows in curiosity. The groom sat astride the horse like an oriental Maharaja dressed in a traditional red turban and a splendid gold suit, his face screened off by orange garlands. My heart went out to him when the cars on the road did not stop to give way. Perhaps they were not accustomed to the spectacle either. They sped off passing a line of seven large coaches parked outside the house, some blasting their horns angrily. When the road cleared the groom was led into the house. The sound of music and the loud beat of *dhol* drums filled the air late into the night. A marquee was pitched on the lawn. I could see its top from my bedroom window. In the morning, the large coaches that had been parked all the way down the hill were gone. Although my family had not been invited, I could tell the celebrations were over.

At school, the arrival of the Asian kids brought new changes. For a start, I stopped going to Chapel on Tuesday mornings and began instead to attend Muslim assembly. One of the new students initiated the gathering. He was a tall, good-looking boy of Pakistani descent. The first time I met him I was standing by myself waiting to catch the bus home when a voice behind me asked if I was alright. I turned to see two dark, compassionate eyes looking down at me. The girls in our class fell in love with him straight away. When he gave his sermons, he spoke passionately and looked deep into your eyes as if singling you out from the rest of the crowd. It drove all the girls crazy. Each week more and more girls gave their excuses and joined Muslim assembly. I noticed most of them weren't even Muslim. Eventually, one of the teachers caught hold of what was going on and sent half of the love-struck devotees back to Chapel.

Muslim prayers began on Fridays too, and with sudden undisguised glee, I realised that this now meant I could skip the queue for fish and chips on Friday at lunchtime. At first, Leila and I were the only girls to attend. Linen bed-sheets were brought in and thrown onto the floor of one of the classrooms as one by one the boys rolled up their sleeves and trousers to perform their ablutions, dunking various parts of their body under the running water of the wash basin in the room. We would cover our heads and take our place behind the boys. When more girls joined, they insisted that we hold our prayers separately. There were only four girls in total but we acquiesced indifferently. Each of us took it in turns to lead the prayers.

Sometimes, my friends peered through the glass windows, pointing in curiosity as they watched us prostrate in sequence. They seemed fascinated by our multi-coloured scarves and the way we swayed up and down rhythmically. My best friend asked me how we all knew when to bow and rise at the same time.

'Your way of prayer looks so graceful,' she told me. 'It's like watching synchronised swimming.'

I laughed when I heard this, thinking of the time when Leila led the prayers and almost sat on my head when she went down to prostrate. We both shrieked with laughter and had to start our prayers all over again.

After school, my father continued to drop us off at the tennis centre and we carried on with our tennis practice, training hard for weekend matches. On the court, my coach made me practise drill after drill, running me from side to side like a yo-yo until I was red in the face.

'Come on!' she shouted whenever I gave up chasing a ball.

I cursed under my breath. During the breaks, we used to chat about trivialities and school life, and sometimes she would complain about this thing she called 'multiculturalism', and how it was eroding age-old English traditions. In particular, she grew very upset when she told me how certain schools had stopped performing the nativity play over Christmas. One Asian mother had complained after her son had been cast as an Eastern King. I remembered how my school had put on the nativity play when I was little and how it had always been considered a great triumph if you managed to get a speaking role. Most of the kids ended up having to dress up as cows or pigs, but I didn't even make it that far, only ever playing the triangle in the percussion team. Still, I used to look forward to Christmas. In December the houses in our neighbourhood would light up with hundreds of fairy lights and people hung ivy wreaths and holly on their front doors. I often wished that my family would put up a pine tree with silver baubles in our living room, or hang stockings and leave mince pies by the fireplace at night like at my friends' homes. But although my parents gave wine and boxes of biscuits to their friends over the festive period, we never celebrated Christmas at home and I never got any presents. The other children would swap gifts with one another in class and once, out of desperation, I even tried to steal a chocolate Santa from a confectionary shop to give to my best friend. When no one else was looking, I snatched the gift-wrapped box from the rack and stuffed it under my jumper. But my mother caught me straight away and made me march back to the counter to apologise, lecturing me during the entire drive home. I blubbered inconsolably in the back of the car, too upset to tell her that I had not intended to eat that Santa myself.

I did not tell my coach I was Muslim. Nor did I did tell her I attended Muslim assembly and Friday prayers at school. I was confused at the time and thought perhaps she did not think of me in the same way she thought of the other Asian kids in my school. I thought perhaps she spoke to me freely in the way she did because I did not look like the other Asian kids, and that with my white skin she thought I was more English, more like her. Otherwise I could not understand how it was she could denigrate the other Asian families so frankly in my presence.

I listened quietly as she told me how London was changing.

'It's not the same London I once knew,' she said. 'It was never like this when I was growing up.'

Every year, more and more foreigners were slipping across the borders, and the country was becoming awash with immigrants who were making a mockery of the welfare state.

But then she would always add, 'But not like your parents. They're different.'

And this part would always confuse me. She would tell me that my family was somehow different, that they were not like

65

the rest of them.

'London is going down in a bad way,' she told me one day. 'I'm leaving before it gets any worse.' The following day, she handed in her notice at the tennis centre and left.

Many years later, I discovered she boarded a ferry and emigrated to a British colony in the south of Spain. I laughed out loud when I heard the news, wondering what the Spanish thought of her.

And then, one day, entirely out of the blue, my father announced, 'We're going back to Kashmir.' Not much else was said. The flights had been booked and my uncle was expecting us. My sister and I were told to bring our tennis racquets.

'We'll have to find a tennis court out there,' my father added, anxious we did not stop our tennis practice while we were away.

When we returned to Kashmir, I must have been sixteen or seventeen. Over ten years had passed since the last visit. We flew into Delhi first. The plane was chock-a-block, crammed to capacity with bawling fidgety toddlers. I cursed my luck when I realised I was to be seated next to a hyperactive-looking three-year-old. During the flight my ears popped and they were still tingling when we disembarked. It was only a fifteen minute taxi-ride from the international airport to the domestic airport, but as soon as I stepped outside, the humidity rushed in to greet me, adding a layer of grease to my face. Delhi was dusty and hot and sprawling with underfed, sweaty people. In our air-conditioned taxi, I sat on one side of civilisation gazing out at the brutal poverty around me. I could not remember anything like it. Hundreds and thousands of people. A blind man, bent and barefoot, walked in the middle of the road heedless of the anarchy around him. In his hand, he held two wooden sticks that rattled against the cars as they sped past on either side. At traffic lights and crossroads, ragdoll-looking children congregated, tapping on car windows before being consumed by the smog of passing trucks. In the midst of it all, a boy with wild hungry eyes appeared from nowhere and began knocking desperately on my window. He wore a vest, and rags or bandages around his temple (I could not tell which), sodden with sweat and dirt. I turned away, ashamed, and felt his shadow blocking my window for what seemed like an eternity. I had nothing to give him. Too cowardly to look up, I sensed his eyes boring into me as if knowing that the only power he had was the power to extract guilt. The driver shooed him away like a fly and I was relieved when we finally flew out to Srinagar.

Centuries ago, a famous English poet challenged the rest of the world with short-lived hubris; *Who has not heard of the Vale of Cashmere, with its roses the brightest that earth ever gave?* When my father was a boy, the Valley was known as 'the Switzerland of Asia'. Srinagar was a lake city and the summer capital of the region and affluent tourists from all over Europe flocked to the centre to spend their days reclining on the decks of the houseboats that lined the banks. On the verandas, the *shikara-wallahs* (gondola men) would flare up their lighters, and puff out smoke as they watched the sun set on the horizon.

'Come to Paradise! Come to Kashmir! Kashmir is the Heaven on earth!'

Such slogans and sound-bites were bandied about and rolled off the tongue as effortlessly as the smiles of street merchants inviting wandering tourists to browse their wares.

In the warmer months, the rose gardens that bordered the lake were packed with holiday-makers picnicking into the early hours. The city was littered with cinema-halls and clubs, and bands came from all over the world to perform in the open air. By early evening, youths left the school grounds to congregate on the banks of the lake, smoking and dangling their legs over the sides. Women walked down the main boulevard wearing cotton skirts and flowery dresses and no one batted an eye. A line of parked motorbikes and cars stretched the length of the main promenade and as the sun set over the lake my father and his friends would flit in and out of the hotels, moving from one bar to the next. Often my father would not return home, staying over with friends or crashing with band members at their hotels. But the times he did, it was always late at night and he would creep in through the backdoor of the White House to avoid waking my grandfather. One of the workers would tiptoe across the landing and gently open the door to let him in.

'Kashmir is the Paradise! Kashmir is the rose of India!'

Srinagar airport was whitewashed with tourist posters, many curling at the edges and seeming rather dated. A driver was waiting for us outside the airport.

"Welcome home, Sir,' he said shaking my father's hand firmly and beaming. 'I hear it has been some time.'

As we drove out of the airport, and our jeep began weaving in and out of reels of barbed wire lying on the roads, a strange feeling came over me and I felt like I was driving back in time. But returning to Kashmir so many years later, the Valley I saw was not the colourful playground I remembered from my childhood. It was not how I remembered it at all. The realisation hit me straightaway. In truth, the drive from Srinagar airport to my uncle's home was a sad homecoming. Something had happened during those missing years. I realised that now, something had happened. Something had irretrievably changed in the Valley, just as something had irretrievably changed in me.

The first thing I noticed were the bunkers. They were everywhere. Ugly, messy-looking enclaves surrounded by barbed wire, with rows of dangling empty bottles, and stray dogs scavenging for food. All across the city, sandbags were stacked up high, and I wondered what was behind them. From small crevices and openings, men in camouflage fatigues and menacing black bandanas peered down the ends of rifle barrels. Their faces softened in amusement when they caught me staring back at them. Curious eyes followed our car as we drove past. In my head, I began to count the soldiers we passed. They were dotted about every hundred metres or so. At one point, a white ambassador car sped past flashing a red siren, flanked on all sides by a convoy of military trucks. With the sudden commotion, I lost count. The soldiers began to blur like a hologram. Eventually, I gave up counting.

As our jeep moved through the city, filtering through a maze of narrow, walled residential lanes, I began looking at the homes hoping to illicit a memory, a familiarity, perhaps recognise a house I may have visited as a child, one that might open up any story into the past. The homes seemed to come from nowhere. They loomed up in the car window, impressive and towering, the older ones especially. In their dilapidation, they possessed an air of former magnificence. They spoke of having seen greater times, defined by their sloping roofs, small patchwork quilts of brick and ancient timber rafts. Some were tucked away behind main roads, some languishing in narrow alleyways. Some were frail and hunched, stained with the marks of age. Some lay vacant, their wooden balconies covered and overhanging like abscesses crusted beyond healing. But most, with stiff resolve, simply seemed to endure. There was a certain quietness about them. They looked abandoned, as if no one had been living in them, and they had been empty for some time. As we drove down one of the side-streets, we stumbled across one where the worst had already come. The building lay gutted and gathering dust, like a carcass in the wild.

My uncle lived next door to my grandparents. When I was young there had been a small green gate separating the properties which swung open whenever my sister and I wandered across to play on his front lawn. As we pulled into the lane, I noticed the gate was no longer there. Instead, a tall brick wall ran along the border of the garden. It was a cumbersome, prison-like structure, detracting attention from the property and seemed to barricade the home from the outside. I wondered why it had been put up. As I sat in the car, staring at the wall, my gaze fell to a thin shaft of light that had begun to mineralise and splinter out along the edges of the patio. I followed it to the top of the wall and there my gaze stopped.

There are many things that memory hoards, many things that are buried away unthinkingly and left for some time until one day they return in a refracted shape or disfigured form, like the faces of strangers you swear you have seen in your dreams, or the turnings you stumble across that keep coming back to you time and time again playing tricks on your mind because you just know you have been there before. At the top of the wall, I stopped. I knew there was something familiar about the place. There was something so intensely familiar. Everything in my body, down to my very own breathing, was beginning to tell me so. I got out of the car and something brushed past as subtle as a falling twig. Perhaps it was just a gust of wind, perhaps a small bird. And then again. Were they birds? I could not see them, but I knew they were there. I could hear them all around me, rustling up above. There must have been hundreds. I paused, unsure of myself and felt something brush past me again. And then, all of a sudden, the air burst into a whirl of colour. Pinks, yellows, reds and oranges; the tones rained down on me like a fleet of heart-shaped arrows. As, one by one, the leaves gradually receded around me, slowly, I turned to face the culprit, and there, across the wall, I saw it, ancient and majestic as ever, my grandmother's chinar tree.

It took me several moments to realise that the gate was not the only thing missing. The great White House was gone.

When I was little, I would spend most of my time floating in and out of the different rooms of the White House passing between the laps of visiting relatives, catching parts of the exchanges between my elders. Most of the time, the conversations were in a language I did not understand and the liquidy sounds would drift and echo through the hallways, flute-like and mellifluous, as my sister and I played together frivolously, barely paying attention to the discussions around us. And yet, somehow, inoffensively, unknowingly, somewhere between languages, those memories were passed down. Somewhere deep, a seed was planted and left, embedded in an unreachable place that would be forgotten for some time, watered by the innermost unconscious only. Otherwise, how was it that many years later, I would still remember them? How was it that when I eventually returned more than ten years on, those memories returned also, pieced together and strangely familiar like the faces of distant aunties and uncles that I saw and recognised but could never quite remember? It ran deeper than logic and reason. It was as if those memories had been deliberately left out for me, as if someone knew that one day I would be coming back in search of them and that when I did, they would be waiting for me, tenderly placed out like pebbles to help me find my way home.

The lake was a short drive from my grandparents' house and had always been a special place when I was a child. As the main hub of activity in the city, it had its own life and character, stretching out to the horizon like an enormous waterpark dotted with rainbow-coloured floats. Whenever my family went to the main boulevard, the *shikara-wallas* would call from their stands offering to ferry us across to their houseboats, and my sister and I would take it in turns to tug on my mother's clothes like small bell-ringers, begging to be taken on a boat-ride. Market-sellers would walk up and down the pavements serenading wavering passers-by as local children splashed along the shoreline glistening in the sun. Further up, men squatted at stalls roasting corn-on-the-cob all day long. My father would stop by one and pick up several sticks and my mother would break one of the

71

pieces into two and give half to me and half to Leila. On the banks, traders came to trade and pleasure-seekers came for pleasure. The lake mingled leisure and labour. It had always been that way.

But on that first day when we drove back to the main tourist promenade bordering the lake, my heart sank. The banks were empty. The *shikaras* with their dull-coloured tatters were not the same jovial boats I remembered. Even the imperialistic houseboats that lined the lake had fallen into a state of disrepair. Paint peeled from their walnut-wood exteriors and algae encroached onto the surface water. The incongruous-sounding name plaques — Robinhood, Claremont, Silver Street, Queen Elizabeth — seemed to reach back to an antiquated time. That evening, I sat on the stone banks in silence, and watched the sun set over the lake.

Atop one of the pink hills that ring the lake, there is an old Mughal fortress which looks down on the whole city. Wherever you watch the sun set over the lake, you can see the fortress rising out of the horizon. The lake curves in a crescent around the hill and it is almost impossible not to look that way. At sunset, every person sitting on the banks is compelled by instinct to look that way. In the evening sky, the fortress glows incandescent as if ablaze. Gazing out across the lake at dusk, the citadel caught my eye. Against the redness of the sky, it looked like it was burning. I could not remember it being there, but when I asked our driver he simply shrugged and told me the fort had been occupied by the army for as long as he could remember. Still, a part of me wondered what the sunset looked like from those ancient ramparts. As I stood leaning against the stone post, lost in my own thoughts, I could not help but feel there was a strange, understated quietness in the air. It was true that even in all its dilapidation, there was something about the lake. The scene was virtually identical to the airbrushed tourist poster I saw at the airport declaring the lake city as 'Paradise on Earth', and yet there

72

was something jarringly different. I struggled to put my finger on it.

My uncle insisted we return home before dark each day. Blackouts were common and access via phone lines intermittent. People still seemed to rely on the shifting movements in atmosphere. The sun set early in the Valley at around seven o'clock. As soon as the light began to fade from the sky our driver would turn on the dipper and the lights inside the car. Each time we drove past an army checkpoint and torches flashed over us, the air became tense and wrought, as if everyone flinched at the same time. I began to notice how the roadblocks assumed a particular sinisterness at night. Large rocks would be put on the roads to slow down the traffic. There was always more checking in the evenings. Our driver was regularly stopped and summoned out of the car by soldiers, and then ordered to remove the boulders from the road. He would do so passively, almost subserviently. In the dark, the soldiers spoke gruffly and seemed on edge and nobody uttered a word to them. At the end of the day, our driver dropped us back at our uncle's home and we would utter a chorus of *Allah Hafiz* (May God be your protector) in the way that people in the Valley bid each other farewell, but I never liked saying goodbye. Our driver lived in the downtown area of the city, a considerable distance from my uncle's house, and there was always an urgency in how his jeep sped off into the dark.

At night, I would lie awake listening to the sound of gunfire in the distance. I had never heard the noise of gunshots in the night before and at first I thought it was fireworks. It would start up around midnight. Sometimes it stopped and there was a long pause before it would begin again. Sometimes during the pauses I heard the howling of stray dogs. In the pitch-black darkness, my mind wandered and I would begin to dream about the scene unravelling outdoors. On my first night, I saw myself standing barefoot like a fugitive outside the house. I saw my shadow make its way to the bottom of the garden, climb the wall and slip away. Outside, I was released into a labyrinth of streets, searching in vain for where the scene was unfolding. The alleys were full of silhouettes and a madness had filled the air, infecting even the dogs as they started to patrol the streets in packs, their eyes narrow and ominous. My shadow continued searching through the night. Where were the soldiers? Who were the boys running away? Was something burning? Was there shouting? There were dreadful canine screams coming from the gutters. Was someone calling out? Was someone calling out my name? My imagination ran wild like the dogs with every unknown.

On that first night, I was woken in the early hours by the sound of a man sobbing. It seemed to be coming from the window. I startled and sat up, listening paralysed from my bed as the sobbing grew louder and more urgent, as the cries of more and more men joined the lament. I was ready to call out when I realised that the siren I was hearing was the *Azan*, the dawn call to prayer. The refrain had carried from a cluster of loudspeakers connected to the pulpits of the local mosques. There must have been at least fifty mosques in the vicinity.

It would be impossible to convey the feeling that came over me the first time I heard the sound of those long forlorn echoes. Until then, I had never heard the sound of a man wail. I had never realised how much anguish a man's voice could carry. These were not the jubilant trumpets I had heard blasted from the sunny rooftops of Istanbul or the steeples in the Middle-East, not an uplifting chorus of praise, not a celebration of life. What I heard was a melancholic, wistful song. That night I lay in bed listening to a broken-hearted ballad sung out as if from a thousand minarets calling — it almost seemed — not for men, but for God Himself. These sobbing men had become the nightingales of Kashmir. I wondered how anyone could bear to listen to such sadness day after day. I wondered how the soldiers in their cantonments could patrol the Valley after hearing it.

74

Perhaps they had grown accustomed to it, dulled even. Perhaps they didn't realise anymore. After some time, I couldn't bear to listen any longer and I tried to cover my ears, tried to bury my head beneath my pillow to block out the cadences of that bottomless despair, but the mosques kept ringing, their alarm loud and clear. The first time I heard them I had tears in my eyes.

On my last day, Leila and I were shopping in the market place when I heard three piercing explosions behind me and turned to catch sight of a four-by-four in flames. The insides were charred black. The sound of firing started up and I rushed into a nearby school. I called out to my sister. Leila ran after me. As the school gates closed behind us, I remember turning to see the road thronging with people. Inside the school, we were ushered into a classroom with a dozen or so other people. We remained there in silence listening to the sound of periodic firing in the distance. Four hours passed inside that room. I remember my throat feeling parched. I was biting down so hard on my lips, they started to peel. But not once did the others around me seem distracted or curious about what was taking place outside. Their faces were glazed, expressionless, and I was struck by the sense of tedium that filled the room. There was a weight in the air, almost a weariness. It was a collective stoicism that brought a lump to my throat and at one point I wanted to shout out and break the quietness and tell them that it was not normal, that it was not right, but a voice inside told me it was pointless. I would soon be gone from this place. I knew that. I would soon return back to the world I came from, and all these people would be left behind. I heard the heavy rumbling of armoured vehicles amassing outside and waited for things to come to their inevitable end. It came. The firing stopped and there was silence. My sister and I waited another hour before the gatekeeper gave the all-clear, and we rushed back home.

Sometimes, when I recall the blank faces that greet me in England whenever I mention Kashmir, I wonder how it must feel

75

to come from a place that nobody knows exists, a place where no one knows who you are or seems to care. Would you start to worry that one day perhaps you might dissolve into abstraction and become just another musical name like Xanadu or Timbuktu, existing in imagination only? Worse still, would you fear you might disappear altogether, without a trace or memory, like one of those cadavers buried across the countryside, erased like history's mistake? Perhaps the time would come when you would need to start pinching yourself just to be sure you were still there.

The day I left the Valley, I knew there were no longer any cinemas or nightclubs in the city. I knew there were no bands that came to play in the summer. At night, I saw the roads become so still that stray dogs grew perturbed by the sight of moving cars. Girls did not wear skirts on the boulevard anymore. It was not safe to draw attention. Many of the women in the city had taken to wearing the *hijab*, some even the full *niqab*, the same black robe worn by women in Saudi Arabia. I could not help thinking they looked like funeral shrouds.

I once asked a group of college girls what they did in their spare time.

'We sit at home,' they said.

When I asked if they grew bored they replied, 'We've gotten used to it.'

In the Valley, things had fallen out of time. Life had moved backwards, not forwards. The present was the past decayed.

On the way back to the airport, our jeep passed a set of words, spray-painted crudely in black, on a wall near a military cantonment: *WHERE ARE OUR LOVED ONES?*

When I embraced my uncle to say goodbye, he told me people were not encouraged to come back to Kashmir. Many didn't. But before I left, I went to the back of the garden and at the foot of my grandmother's chinar tree, I tied a ribbon to the

76

lowest branch. I hoped one day they would return though, and whatever it was that happened in the Valley would be put right. I hoped that one day the path back would flow as effortlessly and seamlessly as it once did when I was a child, and that on that day the Valley of my childhood, and the White House with it, would emerge from the ashes like a phoenix.

I left the Valley wanting everyone to know about the Valley, and yet wanting to hide it. My memories of the White House haunted me. With my return, so did the memories, vague and illusive at first, incomplete, cut short, always somehow broken. In my sleep, I would find myself back in that home, sometimes in the lounge, sometimes standing by my grandfather's bookshelf, other times in my old bedroom or sitting by the dowry chest gazing at its spiralling bulbuls as they flew out and vanished between lines. But most often, I would be sitting beneath my grandmother's chinar tree, as if waiting for her return. I would dream the same dream again and again, stalking the exact same spot, retracing my footsteps, unable to let go. But even in my dreams, the White House was always peopleless, and I inhabited my memories alone.

Only once was that solitude interrupted. It was night-time and we were driving on the road en route to another tennis tournament, somewhere outside London. It must have been somewhere far from the city because there were stars in the darkness and I knew they only ever came out in the country. One of the stars was twinkling mysteriously and I had been staring at it for some time. After a while, I realised with a little disappointment it was just the flashing signal of an aeroplane blinking intermittently and I began to drift off to sleep. In my dream, I was playing outside the White House when the rockets went off. I heard them in my sleep. They erupted in the sky and I turned to see them take the White House with them. The house exploded in the air and shattered into a myriad of firecrackers, scattering and dispersing into thin air. I watched the sparks morph into fire lanterns and float down in the darkness, one by one falling and extinguishing all around me. Each time I ran and tried to catch them, they dissolved at my touch. I was still trying to catch the broken pieces when the car jolted suddenly and shook me back to reality. I woke dazed and confused, not knowing where I was, only longing to see that house once more.

But there was nothing left. There was nothing there now. It was as if it had never existed, and all the people in it — my grandparents and everyone else — had never been there. What had happened? What had happened during those dark years that no one spoke of? What sort of unimaginable things had unfurled in that sick garden that everyone seemed to know of and conspire in? The White House, the great White House, that centuries-old heirloom with its walnut-wood banisters and cascading staircases, those balconies which must have heard the tumbling laughter and footsteps of so many children and grandchildren, so many comings and goings … my beloved White House, what had become of you?

Before we left Kashmir, my father insisted we visit our ancestral shrine in the old city. My grandparents were buried there. The shrine lay in the heart of the downtown area, tucked away in a coil of tapering alleyways. Once a river passed through the city and small-brick houses were built on the fringes of the banks with connecting wooden bridges. The bridges were lined with stalls. From either side of the banks, wide stone steps led down to the waterfront and were once used as a popular trading hub as goods passed down the river by boat. Over time, the river had been filled, leaving only a concrete road to mark the path of the former channel.

For the most part, the old city seemed resistant to change. Some of the backstreets looked as if they had not been touched for centuries. The buildings were still fresh with the marks of their history, their signs only needed to be read. As we drove past shattered glass windows and gutted buildings, our driver narrated their histories, explaining how the low doorways traced back to a time of Afghan rule when horsemen rode into homes to snatch local girls forcing the residents to lower their entranceways and the reason why a beautiful stone mosque always stood empty. Craftsmen and artisans sat conversing in open shop windows. I saw the unwashed red stain of pro-freedom graffiti rise and fall from view, and sandbags piled like bricks behind windowsills. A little blonde boy leaned out of a second-floor window, spat and disappeared. Seconds later, he re-emerged smiling.

The shrine was nestled down a narrow trading street, not more than a stone's throw from the actual burial ground. It was here that the men of my family and their spouses were laid to rest. Inside, my grandmother's grave lay beside my grandfather's. Their bodies had been lowered in one after the other. The locals knew about the shrine. They knew about my grandfather, and for the very first time I heard people pronounce my surname in the right way. They seemed to know and recognise it. I saw it written in several places and wondered what sort of man my grandfather was that his name was so widely known.

I got out of the jeep. The lane was dusty and the sun intense that day but I was wearing my mother's white cotton *shalvar kameez* and the garments were loose-fitting and cool. As we made our way to the entrance gate, I draped the *dupata* around the back of my neck. Inside, we found the shrine in a state of abandonment. Tall grasses and reeds had grown unimpeded and I could barely distinguish the plain stone plaques marking out the graves. Purple irises had sprung up all over, indiscriminately peppering the profusion of grassy moss. Whatever it was that had happened during my absence, it had not left even the dead in peace. My father spoke brusquely in Kashmiri to an elderly caretaker and thrust lots of rupee notes upon him. One of the other caretakers informed us that ladies were not allowed to enter the graveyard where the tombstones lay and my mother shook her head in evident dismay. It seemed to be a new development. But the caretakers of the shrine were poor, time-ravaged people. Their livelihood depended on the goodwill of visitors and we did not have the heart to protest.

Reluctantly, my mother, my sister and I waited behind the wire fence while my father entered the restricted area. I covered my head and lowered my veil. Through the netting, I watched my father pad softly across the tall grass until he reached his mother's resting place. As he stood there, I wondered what I would say to my grandparents if I ever saw them again. What language would I use to greet them? What language would we converse in? Where would our words meet? It would not be Kashmiri, I knew that, but then I wondered whether English would be the right language either for I remembered my grandmother had conversed very little in this tongue. I raised my head and glanced at my father, wondering what language his thoughts came to him in.

The last time I saw my grandparents, deep down I had known something was wrong. I knew because every year my family travelled to Kashmir to see them, and that particular year it had been different. That year, my grandparents came to see us. Perhaps in some way they knew. It was the first and only trip they made to England and it had felt suddenly strange seeing them in Alderton Hill, an inverse of how things should have been. It felt somehow unnatural. Away from their familiar environs, I remember thinking they looked foreign, almost anachronistic, displaced by time and geography. My grandfather used to take long walks in the garden by himself and I would often spy him from our bedroom window half-consumed by the shrubbery and wonder what he was doing out there all alone. I would watch him as if watching a rare bird. Even in his final years, he was a noble-looking man. I remember thinking it was in the depths of our garden among the soft slopes and bushes that he seemed most content and most present to me. It struck me that perhaps those walks just reminded him of home.

Well, over a decade had passed and now I had returned. I had come back at last.

'I've come back,' I whispered through the wire netting. Water began to rise at the back of my eyes. 'Dada … Dadi … I've come back.'

I was too late, I was far too late, but I had come. I had not forgotten. As I lowered my head and cupped my hands, imagining the scene that must have played out in my absence many years ago, I slowly began to repeat the only words I knew we were likely to share and know, words that belonged to neither of us and which I did not fully understand, but which my mother had taught me and I had committed to memory long ago.

> *Bismillaah ar-Rahman ar-Raheem*
> *Al hamdu lillaahi rabbil 'alameen*
> *Ar-Rahman ar-Raheem Maaliki yaumid Deen*
> *Iyyaaka na'abudu wa iyyaaka nasta'een*
> *Ihdinas siraatal mustaqeem*
> *Siraatal ladheena an 'amta' alaihim*
> *Ghairil maghduubi' alaihim waladaaleen.*

(In the name of Allah, the Most Gracious, the Most Merciful.
Praise be to Allah, Lord of the Worlds,
The Most Beneficent, the Most Merciful,
Master of the Day of Judgement.
Thee alone do I worship; and Thine alone I ask for help.
Guide me to the Straight Way,
The path of those whom Thou hast favoured,
Not the path of those who earn Thine anger nor of those who go astray.)

81

I returned to England with growing pains of a different kind. They were the kind that did not show.

At school, I grew restless. The textbooks I read taught me about medieval moats and baroque windows, Shakespeare's Hamlet, Hardy, and bombastic English kings, but nothing of the other histories I had been exposed to. I found there was no one I could share my experiences with, not even the other Asian kids. In one corner of the Sixth Form common room, among half-finished energy drinks and plastic burger cases, a group of Indian boys hung out lounging on the sofas, listening to loud rap music. They wore their hair slicked back with gel and adorned themselves in gold jewellery, speaking of themselves as 'brown people' and seemed wrapped up in some sense of 'brownness' that I found impossible to relate to. I didn't even look 'brown'. At first they were surprised to discover I was Asian and joked about my fairness.

'She ain't a coconut. Ain't even brown!'

One of the boys asked about my background. But when I mentioned Kashmir, he snorted back, 'You mean India. We own you!'

I thought perhaps he had visited the Valley too, but when I asked, he just shrugged.

'Full of Paki terrorists!' he spat, and the other boys laughed.

They did not seem to know the Kashmir I knew.

It did not take me long to realise that with these boys, their parents had impressed upon them a culture that did not reflect their reality, and the trips back to their native lands only bored and further alienated them. There was nothing to do. They would sit at home all day with the fans on full blast, venturing out every now and then only to be rotated around a conveyor belt of relatives' homes. When they spoke of their roots, it was always with a sense of distance, sometimes even condescension as if everything that came from that part of the world was somehow tarnished and regressive. In the common rooms, they lit up and smoked, swearing, laughing and tossing about multiple mobile phones indifferently; one for their family, one for their friends, sometimes even one for their girlfriends. Outside the strictures of their homes, they rebelled and did all sorts of things behind their parents' backs, and at times it seemed more than just the flightiness of youth, as if the defiance was spurred on by some conscious attempt at cultural disaffiliation, some deliberate act to breakaway. But when their parents came to school on Open Days wearing *saris* and open-toe leather *chappals*, they would fall quiet and become demure again, shrinking back and shuffling awkwardly as if ashamed to be seen with them.

With the Pakistani kids I knew, it was almost the exact opposite. The youngsters seemed overly affected by the trends and habits of their ancestral cultures despite somehow never having witnessed them. The girls wore headscarves and ballooning gowns and the boys seldom mixed with others, only occasionally breaking away from their clique to sermonise and complain that there was no *halal* meat in the school canteen.

I found myself struggling to fit in. As my engagement with tennis grew, my visits to the mosque declined and grew less familiar. After puberty, bending in prayer became an awkward, self-conscious exercise. I would find it a strange, uncomfortable process covering up each time, having just spent the morning running about on a sports court in a t-shirt and skirt, slipping tennis balls into my knickers without even thinking twice. Inside the mosque, I became increasingly conscious of the need to cover up. Even while I prayed, I felt the bottom of my legs come under close scrutiny from the women around me. On one occasion, a lady tapped me on the shoulder and pointed disapprovingly at my prayer veil which had loosened to reveal a strand of my hair. I found myself concentrating less on praying and more on the motions of prayer. The ladies' section began to feel disorientating, with small kids running riot and a never-ending chorus of crying babies. I struggled to bring myself close to God and in the midst of the clamour I would peer down enviously at the solemn congregation in the men's section below. In the frustration, my own prejudices would come alive and I would look to my left and then to my right, thinking there was little in common between me and the heavily-clad women on either side.

In newspapers, in magazines and on the television, I never saw a Muslim that looked like me. On Friday afternoons, youngsters congregated outside the mosque sporting long beards and traditional short-cut *kurtas*, exposing incongruently branded Adidas trainers and Reebok Classics underneath. When I switched on the television, I watched an Asian girl in a tight headscarf win the right to wear a long robe to school and proclaim her court ruling as a victory for Muslims looking to preserve their identity in the West. She was eloquent and fluent with a perfect English accent, but I failed to understand how a piece of cloth had anything to do with my identity. As the images of veils and *burqas* began to proliferate and multiply, plastering themselves over news channels and headlines and gathering in number on the streets, I started to find myself imprisoned by these symbols. They began to represent something exclusionary, something superficial and rigid that made me feel like an outcast. The world I knew and saw and felt was more diverse, more complex, full of feeling and belief that could not be reduced to token or monotype. And I knew that, because every day I saw it in myself.

And so, I guess that was how it began, how I started to see myself as separate from the other Asian kids. At home, I even began speaking about them with a sense of distance and my mother would often check me.

'Well, what do you think you are, Liyana?'

'But, Mama, you don't understand. I don't think I am like them.'

And then I would falter as I tried to pinpoint the

84

differences. How could I explain it?

After Kashmir, I realised there was a huge part of me that had been searching for something which had found its definition there. There was something out there that called to me, something I struggled to articulate and started to revert back to when I could not find the answers. I realised that all this time I had been longing to fit, to pin myself to something, to be attached to something that made sense of it all, and each time I had somehow fallen short. But now, whenever I filled in the ethnic minority surveys and Government-sanctioned diversity forms, I started ignoring the 'British Asian–Indian' and 'British Asian–Pakistani' options. A catch-all box labelled 'British Asian–Other' scooped up all outstanding, hyphenated and fragmented Asian identities and I began to tick this box, writing down in the space provided, 'BRITISH KASHMIRI'.

I had never heard of this identity before. In truth, I did not understand it. But by that time, I was sure of one thing; no one else understood it either. Somewhere out there in the steep mountain passes, physical battles were being waged to define it. Rightly or wrongly, Kashmir became an explanation. Kashmir was an anomaly, an aberration, a misfit, a maverick, a minority. Whatever it meant, it seemed suitably fluid and amorphous to take me into its folds. It spoke out to my differences. It offered a retreat, a space to escape everything else that did not seem right, a reason for my contradictions, for everything that did not seem to conform. It offered me the chance to forge an identity of my own.

One evening at the dining table, my father joked that there were too many Asians in Alderton Hill and it was time to move out. Six months later, we packed up and left.

From then on, I returned to Kashmir every year. A strange kind of urgency accompanied each journey. I could not understand it. I found myself prepared to drop everything for those trips without fully comprehending why. Each year I would look forward to the visits a little more. Kashmir called to me. I had found something precious, something ephemeral. The Valley had the quality of a hallucination. There was something otherworldly about what I saw out there. It was so unlike anything else I had known, it verged on the make-believe.

Outside the city, there were parts of the Valley that were still as resplendent as ever. My father would never let us stay at home. In the morning, we would leave early and drive out to the country and it would not be long before endless tracts of lush terrain began to unfurl around us.

'This is the real Kashmir,' my father would say with a sigh.

It was the Kashmir of his childhood, and we drove through rural belts that looked as if they had not changed for centuries. In the first light, the surroundings glowed translucent and made the grass flicker with gold. There were long willowy tunnels of greenery where horse and cart trundled along as the transport of the day. Bakers sat in shop windows with baskets of hot bread. Roosters heralded the morning. Gaggles of geese waddled leisurely across the roads. Our driver stopped the car and we followed him on foot as he went from home to home in search of a villager who would sell his goose. Eventually, we made our way into a small marketplace and a white-feathered bird was held down and slaughtered on the spot. It was plucked and put into a plastic bag. At the next village I was relieved to hear that the geese were not for sale.

The further we drove, the more accustomed I grew to the soldiers peppered across the greenery. Sometimes they were resting under trees or squatting in boredom in the mustard fields. Some had removed their helmets. Some were yawning sleepily. Some were just staring out at the prolific nature rustling about them, their guns resting beside the trunks of trees. Alone against the elements, they looked harmless. They looked less like men of war and more like sons, brothers and fathers from distant parts of India. God knows what they thought of this place so far from the villages and cities they had grown up in. The natural world billowed forth swallowing them up in its fecundity.

We made our way through copious stretches of fluorescent green paddy and travelled to far off farming villages. Along the roads I saw jade shrouds tied to trees and wondered what they meant. Shrines materialised around corners decorated with Sufi ribbons. We stopped at tea houses and sat on makeshift stools by the roadside while tea was poured for us in miniature glass tumblers. People were curious to know where we came from and when they heard my father speak Kashmiri, their faces broke out into enormous smiles. My sister and I would watch and listen with strained faces, every so often pleading with my father to translate.

'The people here are simple people, so innocent,' the owner of a small eatery told us. 'They would hear aeroplanes in the sky and think they were thunderbolts.'

He came from an agricultural village near the border. A few years back, armed men stormed his home and shot dead his wife and brother-in-law. It did not seem right to ask why. Three of his young children witnessed the act. He took out a small briefcase and showed us photographs of his family as they had been found. The pictures were crude and uncensored and my father quickly turned away. I caught a glimpse of a picture of three small children inset, looking dazed.

Despite his meagre livelihood, the owner refused to let us pay for the tea, and when we tried to leave a tip discreetly, he chased us to our car. He smiled and held his hand to his chest.

'*Shurmind cheu keraan*' (Please do not embarrass me), he insisted, returning the notes to my father.

We were the first outsiders to have come to his tea house in a long time. As we coursed through the hilly pastoral land, I watched men and women labouring in the fields and saw an elderly man ambling along counting prayers on his fingertips. Farmers toiled in the fields husking rice and I winced at the thought of how effortlessly I had wasted the same grains on my plate. Their bodies moved through the fields with such grace. There was a purity about those scenes that made the locals look like figures in a Renaissance painting or a Hardy novel and I was reminded of what the owner of the eatery told us. From the front of the jeep I saw my father shake his head sadly.

'There was a lot of pain still in that man,' he said. 'Didn't you see how much he wanted to tell his story?'

We carried on, driving through the famous saffron fields and the great apple orchards of Kashmir. I saw hundreds of thousands of apple trees, their boughs hanging low with the weight of ripe fruit. Beneath the shade of a tree, I glimpsed the outstretched form of a sleeping *chowkidar* (watchman). The apples were rosy and tempting and I wondered what would happen if I paused to pick one. Would the world come crashing down? We crossed rivers running parallel to little mud and burnt brick villages filled with green-eyed children. They stopped and stood peering at us from behind long dark lashes before darting away again. When the sunlight caught their eyes, they sparkled like emeralds. Some told me the redheads and blondes among them were descendants of Alexander the Great's dispersed Macedonian army, others said they were the children of the Lost Tribe of Israel. The roads crumbled into dirt tracks and our jeep jolted up and down. I saw boys swimming in milk-coloured canals. Some lay half-naked and waterlogged on the dark tarmac roads drying themselves in the sun. Their trousers, shirts and slippers lay in the open, and a wet trail of small footprints ran all the way down to the edge of the water. When they spotted us in our jeep, their faces lit up with smiles and they waved. I smiled and waved back.

There were curving roads that circled the mountains like

halos and took us higher and higher until we reached beautiful plateaus of flowers, some similar to those I had seen in the gardens of England. Others broke from the soil, so exotic and assorted in nature, a palette of bold colours, it was as if they had been gathered from across the breadth of the land. In the alpine meadows, masses of white and yellow blooms quilted the earth. Dense patches of purple forget-me-nots and creeping lupins grew unfettered on the cliff banks, and the higher up we went, the more blossoms we encountered.

My uncle once said, 'If you go into the mountains you will find God there. You will see things that will change your life forever.' And he told me stories about rocks the size of football pitches bursting with wild flowers and places where you could look down and touch the clouds with your fingertips.

'There are places where you can stand with one foot in the sun and one foot in the rain,' he told me. 'Places where the lakes flow into the sky and you cannot say where the earth recedes and the heavens begin.'

Shepherds and their flocks passed us by indifferently. They moved in families as if travelling from a different time. I watched in wonder as they climbed down the rock-faces with the ease of their mountain sheep, carrying their children and blankets on ponies behind them. Two ruffle-haired toddlers were fastened back-to-back on a donkey by rope. Their small bodies bobbed up and down along with the rest of the tethered possessions.

On our last day in the mountains, we pulled into a lay-by for lunch and my mother took out a box of sweetmeats and a stack of *paranthas* (unleavened bread) wrapped in aluminium foil. As I sipped on my tea, my gaze fell upon a family working in the fields. They were a group of men, women and children spread across different generations. It could have been a scene pulled from the pages of a fairy tale. In the afternoon sun, I watched, mesmerised. One elderly man, in particular, caught my eye.

Slightly removed from the others, he was resting in the shade, and I guessed he must have been the patriarch of the family. Never before had I seen someone so striking. His beard was long and white. It was a pure, clean white like the whiteness of snow. His eyes were bluish green. They seemed to change colour. Blue like the lakes and green like the valleys. His features were aquiline and handsome. They made me think of the mountains that towered around me and the outstretched wings of kites soaring against the sky. Never before had I seen someone so inseparable from their surroundings. Something came over me. Perhaps it was awe. Perhaps it was a touch of envy. I remember thinking he belonged so perfectly there.

'What was real?' I asked myself again and again. What was real? Was the Valley real? Were those people real? What was real? Back in England, life was so different. Each time I left the Valley, I thought I would lose it again. Days, weeks, months passed. Away from that place, I began to pine for it. I feared I might forget it or that it would disintegrate into nothing and like some waking dream, all that I had known there would disappear once more.

And yet, Kashmir always waited for us.

'The Valley is missing its twins,' our driver would write to us and I would picture the pretty pink and white lilies bobbing up and down on the water and the solitary splendour of the Mughal arch standing against the liquid sunset in the middle of the lake.

Even the people became landmarks. In my mind, I saw them locked against the landscape in a state of eternal stasis, like the old woman who sat crossed-legged on the footbridge stitching rags surrounded by sleeping dogs, or the man who waited by the roadside just before the bend in the lake selling corn-on-the-cob behind a skein of smoke. In the afternoon, a young boy came out onto the steps of a small blue-topped mosque by the Bund. At *Maghrib* time, he vanished and from the minarets I could hear his mellifluous voice filter across the backwaters of the Jhelum. Each year I would find them transfixed to the same places, as if untouched by time.

The more I went back, the more I felt the Valley open itself up to me. Word travelled freely in the Valley and it did not take long before people started to recognise us. They seemed to spot us from a mile away.

'*Koshur coour! Koshur coour!*' (Kashmiri girls! Kashmiri girls!).

Strangers came up to us and asked about England as if it were some fabled land. People seemed curious to know, offering their stories of the past, some even extending cuttings, photographs, letters, whatever remnants or memorabilia they had of their connections to a former, better time.

'I once knew a Britisher from Birmingham!' one man declared proudly before proceeding to flood me with a list of monosyllabic names, asking me if I knew any of them.

In this strange meeting-place of memories, I became an accidental messenger and was invited in by a hotspotch of people: *autorickshaw-wallahs*, *shikara-wallahs*, shopkeepers, meat-vendors, restaurateurs, bakers, schoolteachers, perfumers and policemen. A cafe owner lit up a cigarette, pulled a chair beside me and told me what life was like in the city. When I bought pastries from the market, the baker winked and gave me an extra bag of coconut macaroons. There was an assumed intimacy in the Valley that at times took me by surprise. It affected everything, right down to the baker's golden macaroons that seemed to belong to the world of fantasy goodies, like pop biscuits, google buns and toffee shocks. They were stiff and textured on the outside, yet soft and sugary on the inside. You had to eat them fresh for them to melt in your mouth, or else they hardened and lost their magical powderyness.

91

'Kashmiri-Englissh girl-ls! Kashmiri-Englissh girl-ls!' the *shikara-wallahs* would shout from their stands when we walked down the main boulevard, and I would turn and smile.

I had a sense of security walking by myself in that place, one I had never felt anywhere else. There was a warmth of such depth and genuineness in my reception, it overwhelmed me. Here, people seemed to know me. My name was a key that opened up a treasure-trove of stories. Strangers would accost me in the street and ask about my family, inviting me back to their homes. Everyone was somehow connected. People wanted to give me something, almost anything of themselves.

'*Kahwa*? Kashmiri tea?' a turbaned-man at the local bank branch offered when I was converting my currency. 'Water?' he insisted when I declined the tea, proceeding to pull out a crumpled packet of wafers from a chest of drawers. 'Biscuit?' An apple rolled out from the drawer, across the desk, and came to a halt before me. The manager looked up beaming, evidently pleased. 'Apple?'

The first time the *shawl-wallah* came to my uncle's home he carried his goods in a cloth bundle on the back of his scooter. My family never bought shawls from the shops. The *shawl-wallah* came from a family of artisans that had been trading shawls for centuries, and he would take tea in my uncle's living room, while my sister and I picked and sifted through his wares. Somewhere in large art emporiums, the same shawls would be sold by middlemen to customers at tenfold the price, eventually making their way onto the shelves of high-end boutiques in the West in places like Knightsbridge and Mayfair. But something seemed to get lost in the journey between places. Displayed in glass cabinets and with expensive price tags, the shawls looked somehow different, suddenly exotic, like cultural showpieces, far-removed from the homeliness and familiarity they had when rolled out in my uncle's living room.

It was different in Kashmir. There the pieces felt alive.

They were part of the tapestry of life that knitted the Valley together, emblematic of the warmth of the people. One time, the *shawl-wallah* took us down a maze of rickety paths into old Srinagar, past rusty bicycles and children playing cricket in the alleys, to his home in the inner city, and we witnessed how the shawls were made. His children laid a white sheet on the floor and served sweet breads and *noon-chai* (pink salt tea). It was there I was introduced to the *shawl-wallah's* father, an elderly man who sat in one corner of the room, needle and thread in hand, deeply engrossed in embroidering a pashmina. He wore thick-rimmed spectacles and I could not help thinking they looked like large magnifying glasses.

'Remember him,' my mother whispered to me as I sat there quietly admiring his austerity against the opulence of his artwork. 'He's the last of his kind.'

It had taken him over three years to complete one of her shawls. The needlework was so fine. When the piece finally arrived in London, my mother draped the fabric around her and I instantly imagined the shawl cordoned off and exhibited under dim lights in some dusty museum.

But the reminders of our life back in England were always within earshot.

'Liyana! Leila! Don't forget your racquets!'

Each time we heard our father's call, my sister and I jumped up like jack-in-the-boxes.

In the Valley, it was always difficult to keep up our tennis practice. On our first trip, my father made enquiries about a court and we even visited a gym, though the staff did not seem accustomed to female visitors. Large eyes followed us as we were shown the facilities and Leila turned to grin at me when she realised the bike machine was just a suspended cycle. The gym smelt of motorbike oil and mothballs. The closed space made us both feel nauseous and so, in the end, we decided to train outdoors.

Just before sunset, when the temperature dropped a few degrees and a cool breeze swept into the Valley, my sister and I went jogging around the lake. Each day, we ran for several kilometres watching the sun as it sank deeper into the water. Along our route, we would pass a line of stationary soldiers. The soldiers were posted every fifty yards or so, standing guard around the whole perimeter of the lake, as permanent as the lampposts. They would laugh as we ran past.

'*Kahan jah rayan ho?*' (Where are you going?), they would call out teasingly and I would pretend not to understand and keep running. Sometimes youngsters trailed us on their motorbikes too, gawking in surprise. But whenever the soldiers caught sight of them, they barked, and then the boys would quickly disperse. Other times relatives would stop their cars and insist on giving us a lift home, looking at us with puzzled, concerned eyes. It did not take long for me to realise that no one else went jogging around the lake. I suppose, after all, my father's insistence on training in front of an audience in England paid off, because we quickly grew accustomed to our new spectators in the Valley too.

Eventually, my father managed to locate a court. There was only one functioning tennis court in the entire city and it lay in a former colonial club that had been taken over by the army. We required special permission to access it and at first, I was nervous about entering the barracks, but the General of the camp was welcoming and even offered his men as ball boys. In the mornings, he took breakfast with my father while they watched us play. My father told him of our tennis competitions back in England. Each time the ball strayed, one of the soldiers would run to collect it and throw it back to us while the General called out in good humour, cracking jokes from the sidelines. One morning, the General came down from the mess a little later than usual, unshaven. There were no jokes that day.

'This place is nothing but a beautiful garrison,' the

General sighed to my father as he drew on his cigarette, and he exhaled heavily as if something was pressing hard on his chest.

Later on, I learnt that one of the men in his battalion had shot himself.

Sometimes during the day, my sister and I returned to the school in the market area where we had first taken shelter, and played basketball with the students. Each year we returned, the boys would be waiting for us, fooling around and teasing one another by the courts as if nothing had changed.

'We live in the paradise. You live in the money!' they laughed, fed by the smog of Bollywood romance. And whenever a girl passed, they serenaded out loud, play-fighting with one another in jest.

But beneath the surface, I sensed a deep unhappiness amongst the youngsters. It was a wound lain bare whenever the conversation moved on to the situation in the Valley. Each time the sound of firing started up in the distance, I listened to the insouciant way the boys spoke of the different types of artillery used, and a great sadness would well up inside. Their dialogue switched from the mundane to the tragic with such effortlessness it troubled me. Peppered amongst the small trivialities of homework and favourite teachers, their conversations drifted into stories of missing cousins and uncles and all the other small reminders of the fragility of life in the Valley.

'When I grow up I want to join the army,' one Sikh boy confided. 'It's the only way.'

At the same time, two other boys told me in earnest of their dreams of visiting Pakistan.

'India is not our home. How can it be when they will never accept us?'

Though they carried identity passes with them wherever they went, none held passports and when I took mine out to show them, I was surprised at just how much they vied with one another to take a look.

At times, I felt an excruciating loneliness define the Valley. Often I would find myself wandering down quiet streets thinking I was alone when all of a sudden the sound of singing would start up. The melodies came from behind tall, gated walls, wafting down the alleyways and disintegrating into the leaves and dust grains. I was struck by the number of orphanages hidden away in the city's alcoves, carefully concealed from sight. One orphanage had been set up not far from my uncle's house and sometimes in the afternoon when the warden came out to empty the rubbish, the gates would open momentarily and I would catch a glimpse of the children cloistered inside — their *pherans* hanging loosely on their small bodies — before the gates closed once more.

Around the banks of the lake, I came across so many teenagers sitting idly, somehow half-invisible, gazing deeply into the lapping water as if it was a gigantic wishing well. An overwhelming resignation seemed to fill the youth and I could not help thinking there was something of Hamlet in each of them. Even when the boys at the basketball courts spoke of their attachment to the Valley, they spoke about themselves as if reluctantly tied to the land by some magic spell, unable to escape its hold. A potent sense of the inseparability of the land from its people pervaded everything. Their fates seemed tragically intertwined.

'I can't help it,' one of the boys sighed. 'It is only because I am here that I am like this. It is only because of Kashmir!'

Over time, more students at the school grew to recognise us. They stopped us in the streets to practise their English and shook our hands. Some requested our email addresses and made us promise to stay in touch.

'You people always forget we people, but we people always remember you people,' one complained.

The girls implored us to stay in the Valley.

'Marry Kashmiri boys-s!' a red-haired girl giggled,

blushing and covering her face as if she had said something wrong.

But there was always an end. Our stay in the Valley was always time-barred. Deep down, no matter how hard we tried, my sister and I both knew it; we never truly belonged. Just like those imported shawls, something irredeemable had been lost in transit. In the Valley, we existed in a creative, chaotic space, swinging pendulum-like from one world to another, somehow breaking the norms of both and fitting in nowhere. If we were welcomed in the Valley, it was always more as a novelty than as a permanence, for the traces of the other world visible through us could only be tolerated there for so long.

'WARNING! YOU ARE UNDER ENEMY OBSERVATION', a road sign cautioned in the alpine passes. Wherever we went, an immovable spotlight followed us, holding us up as two cultural artefacts from a foreign land. It was a spotlight that both inhibited and protected us, at once granting us immunity and at the same time warning those around us not to come too close because we were, after all, different. For if we crossed through a tangle of conventions and expectations, it was always because we could do so freely and almost without consequence, safe in the knowledge that there would always be a bridge waiting to grant us safe passage to another side.

Even so, when it came to leaving, my sister wept like a child. 'But I don't want to go!'

My uncle protested in our favour to my parents, and a tender fuss was made over us.

Why couldn't we stay?

It became almost like a ritual. On the drive back to the airport, I would look out the window in silence, trying to take in as much as I could in those final minutes. At the airport, our jeep followed the rest of the cars through the maze of security barriers. A soldier stopped us to inspect our tickets and surveyed us from head to toe. I lugged my suitcase past uniformed men

97

and automatic rifles like a robot, handing over my passport and raising my arms automatically whenever a voice called out for a security check. Each time I passed through the scanners and heard the beeps of the metal detectors as they skimmed over my body, I thought perhaps I exited the Valley a little weightier than when I first arrived, for I always left with a heavy heart.

Back in Alderton Hill, Leila and I picked up from where we left off and fell straight back into our regular routine, rotating between school and the tennis centres. My father continued with the process of dropping us off and picking us up after work. I chatted to my friends on the steps of the sports pavilions as if nothing had changed, catching up on the latest gossip and playing cards during the breaks. I laughed and joked about frivolously. But I never mentioned Kashmir. I never told anyone. Perhaps there was a part of me that thought there was no point. No one would understand anyway. Only a week ago I had been training in an army barracks in the most militarised zone in the world, surrounded by soldiers and endless miles of barbed wire. I had trod over a mound of earth that had entombed the lives of so many thousands of people and had irrevocably changed the course of millions more. The grit on my trainers was proof. How could anyone know all the thoughts that flowed from that experience, the emotions that I had felt in that place, the things that I had seen, the memories that had been stirred? How would they ever understand? It was as if I had come from another world.

Sometimes out of the blue, my sister and I received messages from the boys in our basketball team. They arrived like diamonds dusted with the shine of a faraway land.

Dear Liyana and Leila, on the pages of roses, with the ink of sunlight, a pen of prayers has written three words for you: WE MISS YOU.

I would read their messages when it rained in England and count down the days until our return.

There is something about old colonial-looking buildings that leaves Asians feeling rather nostalgic. Maybe they feel like they are coming home again.

When my father accompanied me to my Open Day at Cambridge University, I could tell he was thinking back to his own school days. I was there because he had been there. Maybe there was a flicker of realisation that this was the fruit of all his years of hard labour. The extra on-call sessions in the hospital. Those additional weekends. The ferrying back and forth between school and the tennis centres. His toil had been to ensure this possibility became a reality for me.

As a child, things had not been so easy for my father, and there had been many years when he and his brothers had gone without meat.

'Poor upper class,' my uncle once described it.

Though my grandfather had been one of the most eminent judges in the Valley at the time, he had also been an honest one, refusing to take the money that may have oiled the path for a more comfortable life. Almost all his earnings were invested in his children's education and, I suppose, in some way, it went to explain my father's fixation on sport since Dada's discipline meant he had never been afforded the opportunity himself.

As a small boy, every day my father would make the five kilometre trek on foot to school, crossing by *shikara* at the banks of the river Jhelum. A small coterie of English ladies lived nearby on the houseboats by the backwaters of the Bund. Most were widows who had decided to stay on in the Valley even after all their menfolk had left. My father would pass them each morning wondering why they had not gone back too. In their perseverance, there was a certain defiance. The women did not socialise with the rest of the locals and did not seem to fit in the Valley. In the mornings, they would sit on the decks of the houseboats drinking tea and chatting amongst themselves.

Each time my father passed, he would wave and politely practise his chorus of *hellos* and *how are yous?* and the women would lower their fans to return the greeting.

Over time, they grew quite fond of my father. One of the ladies often invited him onto her boat for tea and told him tales of life back in England, sometimes dipping into her purse and rewarding him with a piece of candy when he did well at school. The lady's family came from a place called Chesterton.

'It's near Cambridge,' she had said. And that was the first my father heard of the university town. 'If you study hard enough, maybe we'll see you there one day,' the lady had chirped, before ushering him on his way to school.

And so, the first time I stood on the trim-cut lawns of that college looking out across the pretty English gardens that lined the river — my father with his champagne flute in hand, and me with my glass of orange juice — part of me knew straightaway that this was where I wanted to be.

At a certain point, I suppose everyone has to leave home. It is the only way if we are ever to build better homes. My grandparents left home. My parents left home. And the time had come for me to leave home. But as the prospective students were being shown around the grounds with their families, I suddenly felt conscious that a part of my father was trying to live vicariously through me. There was a wide-eyed, curious boy following my every step. I felt him jumping up and down trying to peer over my shoulders. And in that moment, my heart melted. I wanted to move to the side and make way for him. I wanted him to be there sharing everything with me.

Cambridge. Beautiful, quaint Cambridge. Like a glass paperweight that you turn upside down and watch as the pretty white confetti falls like snow on a miniature town below. Cambridge was just like that, a temporary world protected in an invisible bubble. I did not have to go anywhere. Everything came to me. All the aspirations of the imagination felt possible during those three years. I felt like I was part of a conspiracy of privilege.

'Enjoy your time here,' one professor told us, 'because it's a dumb world outside.'

And it was like a narcotic, because when he said those words, I was sure everyone in that lecture hall sucked them in and believed them.

Cambridge passed like a dream. Each year glided by like a sequence of beautiful vignettes. At times, I felt the need to pinch myself. In the autumn, little street lanterns lit up the narrow cobblestone pathways and the gardens turned a delicious orange-brown colour. In the first term I wanted to photograph everything. The perfect symmetrical green quads. The cute humped-back bridge. The impressive stone archways. Sometimes, a low-lying mist gathered in the early morning and from my bedroom-window it looked like a thick layer of cloud was rolling over the lawns. I bought a second-hand bike from the market and cycled in and out eager to see as much of the town as possible. Most of the college entrances had heavy wooden gates with tiny little flap-doors cut out of them and I had to bend my head to enter. I would flash my university card at the porters, smiling nervously. At times, I felt as if I was trespassing. Entering each college ground was like discovering a secret garden. As soon as the flap-door slammed behind me, the hustle and bustle of street-life was shut out. Inside those buildings, it was so quiet, part of me felt the need to tiptoe.

In the winter, the town turned white. A true glass paperweight. A thick layer of snow coated the brown earth like the icing on a rich Christmas cake. Cambridge was never more magical than when it snowed. It snowed each of the three winters I was there. Long icicles formed in the shape of pick-axes along the edge of my window, and parts of the river froze over. During the day, there were snowball fights in the courtyards. It got dark early and students complained about the dimly lit streets.

Sometimes the choir gave midnight services and in the early hours the sound of singing wafted through the air past the Chapel. We took our tutorials in tall-ceilinged rooms with hearty log-fireplaces. The rooms smelt of old books. Our tutor would take out a heavily thumbed copy of some Shakespearian play or some piece of eighteenth-century literature and begin reading out loud.

Sometimes I experienced moments of extreme self-consciousness and became convinced that somehow a mistake had been made. I was not supposed to be there. I was a counterfeit, an imposter. What the hell was I doing in Cambridge talking about dead Englishmen and abstracted concepts like freedom, love, tragedy and suffering? What had I known of these things when there were people I had met who knew so much more about them? And why did one girl in our group always have to read Christianity into every single passage of literature we picked up?

Other times, I was overcome with awe as I sat in those enormous armchairs. I would study the walls, the ceilings, the mantelpiece, the shelves, the books, everything in the room and feel like I was breathing in history. I wanted to pick up the phone and tell my father how wonderful it was.

If it be now, 'tis not to come; if it be not to come, it will be now; if it be not now, yet it will come …

A sense of calm would come over me and I would feel reassured and empowered. Everything was as it should be.

In the spring, a line of eight little ducklings fell like dominos into a big puddle on one of the college grounds and the picture made the front page of the student newspaper. Jean Marie le Pen, the right-wing French fascist, came to speak at the Union building and protestors egged his car. Announcements were made and a horde of global conglomerates and investment banks set up on campus dangling free pens and flashing key-rings. I took away several business cards and a stack of glossy brochures.

Warm spring showers breathed fresh life into the gardens as a mass of daffodils sprung up along the walkway to our tutorials. In the morning, it was like passing a magnificent yellow-headed crowd. I plucked a few of the blooms and put them in a vase in my bedroom, not realising that the gardens were out of bounds to the students.

In the college common room, a pretty Jewish girl with a small nose-stud asked me to join her society. She was dating one of the senior boys and the pair were activists campaigning for justice in Palestine, like John Lennon and Yoko Ono for peace.

When summer came, the market began selling boxes of king-size strawberries. Tourist-filled coaches pulled up at the central bus station and throughout the day, huddles of sightseeing groups clustered around different parts of the town sporting oversized sunhats and black Canon cameras. They took photographs of random things like lampposts and letterboxes.

But summer was also exam time and for a month, the entire student body went into hibernation. The porters locked up the towers. I grew accustomed to the sight of sleeping-bags in our college library and drowsy-eyed students shuffling in and out to refill their coffee-mugs. Sometimes they wandered into the common room still wearing their pyjamas.

I discovered my perfect study spot. In the afternoons, I would snuggle up with my books in one of the alcoves of our college library and lose track of time. I read so many books in that nook, flicking through the works of so many writers. Marlowe. Byron. Tennyson. Flaubert. Ruskin. Neruda. Aeschylus. Herodatus. Homer. Gide. Camus. Racine. Rushdie. Shelley. In the afternoons, the sun would spear through the windows and cover me in a shower of warm light. Sometimes I nodded off with the pages still open.

As soon as the last exam was over, the town exploded like a giant party-popper and in no time at all the students were back out again strewn all over the lawns carousing merrily. A group of boys came out in their whites to play croquet and made me think of my tennis days. In the week before the summer holidays, the famous May Balls began and long queues of revellers formed outside the college gates dressed flamboyantly in tuxedos and ball gowns of assorted colours and designs while tourists eagerly snapped away at the spectacle with those ubiquitous Canon cameras.

At my first May Ball, the gates flew open and a full orchestra started up in welcome. Inside, the college grounds were utterly transformed. White marquees were pitched on the lawns where all sorts of new-fangled delicacies were served, from oysters and caviar to cinnamon churros and white-chocolate fountains. By the banks of the river, boatmen offered to take visitors midnight-punting. Little lanterns hung from the ends of the boats and petals were thrown into the water while waiters attended to romancing-couples with chocolates and roses. I sauntered past ice-statues, casinos, magicians, fairground rides, jazz bands, opera singers, jugglers and fire-eaters, almost tripping over a punt full of champagne bottles. My friends laughed, assuming I was tipsy. A few boys jumped into the river and splashed about while a group of onlookers cheered them on from the bankside. At midnight, the fireworks went off and everyone looked to the sky to see a rainbow of colour erupt over the darkness. I could not help thinking that something about those May Balls reminded me of my childhood.

There in Cambridge, I met many of my dearest friends. They came from all corners of the globe: Japan, South Africa, France, Greece, Scotland, Sri Lanka, Morocco, Malaysia, Egypt, Turkey, Singapore, Iran, South Korea, and so many more countries. I found myself travelling through people and saw traces of different worlds marked all over them. The more people I met, the more worlds I felt jostling with one another. I felt them coming together like pieces in a great mosaic. I began to flood myself with people. More and more people. Somehow in our bubble, we were all interconnected. It felt organic and natural. As I sat in coffee shops chatting away about everything and nothing until the early hours, I felt myself slowly opening like a lotus.

When my friends came over, I sprinkled almond flakes at the bottom of my teacups just like it was done in the Valley and served them yellow saffron tea.

My friends would always comment, 'This tea is *so* delicious. Where did you get it from?'

The saffron had been hand-picked from the fields of Pampore, just south of the Valley. Our driver had stopped the car in a lay-by just opposite the fields while I bought several grams from a roadside stall. The farmer had weighed the red papery strands on a metal scale before putting them in a box. The fields were still brown and fertile at that time, stretching out for acres like a quilt of undulating humps. Within days, the purple crocuses would begin to emerge from the plains and cover the earth in a robe of colour.

I told my friends the tea came from Kashmir. It was the first time I felt brave enough to share Kashmir with others.

I kept on returning. When the summer breaks came around I was always ready, expectant and overly excited, my suitcase packed. Leila would be waiting too. She didn't need to say anything, I knew she felt the same. There was a strange convalescent quality to each trip we made. In the Valley, life was so bare. Standing on those solitary peaks or by those lonely streams, or just walking through the meadows as the rabble of butterflies passed. I felt so close to creation. I felt it in my skin. It was a tranquillity that spread from the core outwards, validated by the surroundings. In the sunlight, I found my cheeks colouring with pinkness. My eyes shone brighter. I never felt so alive, and it left me feeling happy. Each year, I thought others might return too.

But despite my enthusiasm, I remained one of the very

few and for the most part the Valley remained a kingdom of lost memories. As soon as I stepped out there, I felt the weight of them, just like I had felt them that first day when I returned. There was something overwhelmingly physical about them. Unbodied and invisible, they gave the air an unnatural heaviness. I was sure I was not the only one who felt them. They haunted the quiet spots of the city, certain places more so than others, and were so palpable in parts it caused me to wonder whether it was not just people that pined for the past, but perhaps places too. One thing was for sure, the Valley had not forgotten its past. It clung to it like a jilted lover, haunted by the ghosts of bygone times. And so, even when things began to improve on the surface, and a fog of optimism crept into the city's tea-stalls and street corners teasing the city with new promise, still the spectre of that peace could not dissolve the feeling of all that had come before. It could not wash away those memories.

The attacks came in winter. It was the first time I saw Kashmir headline in a national broadsheet, and the unexpectedness of seeing it appear so brazenly in Western print took me by surprise. There were images too, but unlike the pictures that cluttered the Valley's tourist boards and posters, these were not pictures of deep mountain glens or piercing blue lakes. Nothing of the green-eyed children or wandering shepherds. Nothing of the lost gardens of paradise over-brimming with their everlasting roses and candied almond blossom. No, my valley came to the rest of the world in black and white, with guns and explosions and the piercing shrill of a broken human alarm. It broke my heart to see it in such a way.

Do you know how many people have been killed in Kashmir? The print cried out.

Ten youths had stormed a popular tourist hotspot in India. They couldn't have been much older than me.

106

'Do you know how many people have been killed in Kashmir?' The words of the gunmen cut through time and space, reproaching me bitterly.

Kashmir.

It was splayed all over the newspapers now. On the television. Plastered across news reels. My Valley. The media had homed in straightaway.

Where was this place?

Who were its people?

What was its history?

Even after I put the paper down, the man's words continued to plague me. Mingled with the vitriol, I recognized something that made me uncomfortable. Something I could not blank out or switch off like the television. It was unmistakable, there had been a terrible despair. I had sensed the same in the Valley on a number of occasions. That reluctant madman. Was he mad before or had we somehow maddened him like the lunatic who grows wilder in confinement?

His words lay bare a rebuke, as caustic as his challenge, as if he had cried out, 'You forgot me there, but I am here now.'

Over one hundred people died in the attack, almost a third of them foreigners. Nine out of the ten gunmen were killed by security forces, their bodies quickly disposed of. The tenth was captured and hanged shortly afterwards.

As the headlines refreshed and the news quickly washed over, I forgot about the story and the man's words. It was only when it resurfaced months later in passing conversation that I was shocked to learn that none of the gunmen even came from Kashmir.

From time immemorial, people have gravitated towards the city in search of work and to make a name for themselves. After my sister and I graduated, I guess we did the same. But while Leila's path took her into a major business centre in Europe, away from me, mine led me back into London.

Returning to the capital, I moved into a one-bedroom apartment in the East End. The block was one of a number of waterside developments that had sprung up around the curve of the river, only a stone's throw from the old docks. Many of the residents were overseas tenants working in the city, renting out the apartments for fixed short-term periods: six months, one year, maybe two years at most before moving on. In the mornings travelling down in the lifts, I brushed shoulders with a miscellany of different countries. Some days it was China, other days Turkey, Russia, Nigeria, Kuwait, Mexico and Brazil. So many nationalities moved in and out of the block, it was difficult to keep track of who my neighbours were.

East London had changed from the collection of old curry houses that I remembered from my childhood. Before, my father would drive us into the East End for Lahori food and the area was home to weekend treats of hot *naans* and spiced meats. When we weren't chasing the endless catalogue of tennis competitions across the country, my father would take us into the area, chauffeuring us past old street lamps and illuminated shop names.

'On this street you have a church, a mosque and a synagogue. All three religions in just one small lane!' And he would tell us about the landmarks and buildings, peppering their histories with his own anecdotal tales.

We would take in everything through the car windows, to the backdrop of Sunrise Radio — 'The greatest Asian Radio Station in the World!' — as it blared out the latest Bollywood hits.

The curry houses were always open. Bursts of liveliness haloed the establishments with a constant ring of light, and trays of sticky orange *gelabis* shone tantalisingly from the glass windows. Inside, Leila and I would take turns to go downstairs and wash our hands. The owners were humble, hospitable people. We had known them ever since we were toddlers when we sat on plastic stools and ate with our hands while the rest of the counters were empty. Though we did not know their names, their faces were familiar, and whenever we entered we would smile politely and say our *asalam-u-alaikums*.

My father spoke to the owners in their native tongue, switching only to English when their sons and nephews worked behind the till.

'*Ek chicken karahi, ek saag gosht, ek pilou …*'

There was no need to look at the menu. We all knew it well. The food always seemed to taste best in the most modest of places, just like home-cooked food. At the end of the meal, the boys brought toothpicks and multi-coloured *spari* and my father would leave cash on the table.

Perhaps because we only ever drove through the area at night, the East End always seemed an aged, darker part of London. At night, we coursed through an endless web of estates and obsolete docks, ploughing through the oldest parts of the city. By the time we reached the commercial district, the textile stores which lined the roads were already shuttered. Against the green and amber reflection of traffic lights, I would peer out at the sporadic patches of life smudged around the fried-chicken shops. Hidden away behind street corners were a few old-looking pubs. Their dim lights made them glow eerily. As we weaved in and out the streets, my father would continue with his stories, telling us about the Kray twins, Jack the Ripper, the red-sleeved ladies of the night and all the other colourful personalities who once made the streets of the East End tremble with notoriety.

'Not a nice area to be wandering alone at night, Liyana.'

I imagined a cloaked, bearded figure stalking the shady nooks and alleyways. The curry houses always seemed to add a heart to the darkness.

But returning to East London after I graduated, there

was a freshness about the place. The old had been replaced with the new. Many of the former *dhabas* had expanded and become popular food hubs in the city, although my favourite *dhaba* had closed down. Somebody told me the owner met with a tragic accident in Pakistan and his family moved back soon afterwards. But the city waited for no one. As the inner city grew, extending its fingertips eastwards, tall buildings and apartment blocks had shot up in the Docklands giving the East End a veneer of new sophistication. Out of the dereliction, Canary Wharf had emerged like a lighthouse, attracting capital investment and developing the locality into a major business district with a number of multinational banks and professional services firms deciding to relocate their headquarters there. Retail and commerce quickly followed, snapping at the heels of prosperity. In the mornings, local buses arrived from all parts of the capital jam-packed with commuters speaking a babel of languages and it was not long before the area became a place of escalators, sliding doors and check-out counters as people came and went in a perpetual rush.

My apartment was walking distance from the old Billingsgate fish market. The port once served as the largest fish market in the world, but now most of the seafood came in by road or was airfreighted from countries thousands of miles away. Early in the morning, buyers came to seek out bargains and in the space of a few hours bushels of oysters, lobsters, tiger prawns, crabs, slippery eels and all sorts of shiny, silver fish were traded on the spot and readied for transportation to destinations all across England. By the time I walked past in the morning, everything was gone and the market long over, with only a few seagulls and the faint whiff of sea air left lingering.

But of all things I loved about returning to the city, the best was the view from my balcony. Although it was a small flat, the windows of the living room opened onto a broad shoehorn-shaped terrace that looked out across the Thames to the

Millennium Dome and bent around eastwards to take in the skyscrapers of the financial district.

The landscape was ever moving, just like the pulse of life it contained. Standing on my terrace on a clear day, I could take in the whole length of the capital. River taxis, private barges and tourist boats ploughed across below me circling the Dome, and all about, small vessels bobbed up and down. At breakfast, around the edges of the shore, I could see the heat rising from nearby homes like pipes blowing out small puffs of smoke. If I was lucky, very early on in the day I would catch huge cruise liners as they passed, blocking out the horizon entirely. A horn would sound and suddenly a ship would appear out of nowhere, majestic and stately, gliding brilliantly into the daybreak. Leaning over the railings, at times I felt so close I wanted to reach out and touch them.

It was no surprise then that my earliest memory of working in the city was of a sky-high meeting room. My interview was in one. A receptionist wearing a tight-fitted pencil skirt and tall red stilettos stewarded me inside a glass room before telling me my interviewers would be along shortly. I took a seat behind a large varnished desk. I was not used to wearing a suit and I remember feeling stiff, like a scarecrow padded out in all the wrong places. All around me, everything was so neat and pristine. A bottle of water stood on the desk in front of me, untouched, and, next to it, perfectly positioned in the centre, a thin glass vase with a single red rose. The rose looked so impeccable installed in the middle of that room as if balancing everything around its orbit. I was convinced it must have been fake. I glanced at the door before reaching out to have a quick feel. The petals were soft and velvety and broke away at my touch, and I quickly withdrew my hand in guilt. On one side of the room, light streamed in through the glass panels and from high above I could look down and see the whole of the city unfolding below. Down on the ground, a crowd of teeming black dots gathered, milling about like ants. It occurred to me that only moments ago I had been just another one of those ants. All at once I felt very small and turned away, staring down at my shoes. They were black and shiny, glaring new. I was still staring at them when my interviewers walked in.

At the beginning, there were many wonderful things about joining the city. There was the newborn rush of freedom and independence, a sense of finally being able to stand on my own two feet. The city possessed a certain intrigue and glamour. It was breathless and sleepless, a modern Mecca full of willowy, good-looking people who came from all over the world. At lunchtimes, they congregated in Waitrose among the aisles as varied as the wraps and sushi bites for commuters on the run. The city meant hearing a dozen different languages and accents on an open-plan work-floor. It meant lofty skyscrapers and revolving glass doors, swipe cards and headsets, extension 6666 for the IT Help-Desk and using the mute button on conference calls. On my way into work, I began picking up skinny lattes for breakfast and chocolate croissants from Pret-a-Manger.

Two computer screens were installed at my desk and in an instant my data multiplied twofold. An international secondee came to sit in the workspace next to me and I leaned over to extend my hand and say hello. Each time new mail was delivered to my inbox a little bleep sounded and made me look up. I started to wonder how I ever managed without Outlook Calendar and my BlackBerry.

I began travelling. At first, it was just the odd excursion, but over time the trips grew more frequent, the time away more protracted. The business promoted mobility.

Adaptability is a key pillar to success.

Bit by bit, everything became compressible into one small, square, black wheelie-bag. Toiletries, hair-straighteners, shirts and tights perfectly folded into the corners. The heels always went in last. On the road, I found myself tapping into a completely different mode of life.

Sometimes I would be gone for days, other times weeks on end. If I was flying out for meetings, I would often leave the weekend before and make stop-overs, spending a few days here or there in interim destinations. Immigration counters became an endless sequence of stepping stones. The pages of my passport began filling with different destinations. I sifted through business-class lounges and crossed continents, passing through cities teeming with other internationals also travelling for work. I started to recognise them in the airports and hotel lounges. They were always checking the time. The more places I visited, the more I saw things that made my eyes bulge: cities fashioned into gigantic pleasure-domes, cities reinvented, cities heralded as the 'capitals of tomorrow'. They stood like fictional lands, spurting out a bamboo-like growth of skyscrapers and cranes across their skylines giving the impression that someone had taken a large architectural pen and drawn all over them, only to return seconds later to reconstruct them again. Between places, I looked out of my cab and saw the horizon pulsating with glittering high-rises and all sorts of outlandish and quixotic constructions.

'You can live the life of a twenty-year-old here until you're fifty!' one woman wearing a short, sequined dress toasted out loud tossing her blonde tresses over her shoulder as she slinked past to a cab.

I was pulled further away from the mainland. Without maps or armies I crossed continents. I visited more places, saw more new countries, dabbled in different modes of life. I travelled to places where the coastlines had been pulled back from the sea and artificial islands forged out of thin air into the shape of palm trees and pseudo-globes, places where I became lost in an army of yellow taxis and found myself being ferried through sprawling concrete metropolises crisscrossed with carriageways and swooping underpasses. At dinner, a waiter pulled out my chair from beneath a vast array of sparkling silverware and polished drinking glasses. One by one, I watched as delicacies from all over the world were brought in and presented. Around the tables, people populated their sentences with currency and I gradually became numb to it all. Each time the waiter rotated the wines, I quietly set aside my glass. By the end of the meal, it felt as if the globe itself was being offered to me on an enormous dessert platter.

As time passed, the city's hold grew firmer. Time squeezed into charts and spreadsheets. The city meant starting to swear like everyone around me. It meant the maddening racket of currency and exchange. Every day, I would watch the screen-rates and check the time zones in Asia, America and the Middle East. It meant walking into the office in the mornings immune to the litter of abandoned cigarette butts on the pavement and comforting a teary-eyed colleague in the afternoon as she struggled to juggle her workload with an early divorce. As the hours stretched on, I started to miss the feeling of daylight against my face. The city meant reading the papers underneath somebody's armpit on the tube and sitting alone in a taxi late at night. It meant eating dinner at my desk in a plastic take-away box and topping up my mug of tea at the coffee machine when the clocks slipped back in time. People started leaving.

'Let's be honest. There's no point pretending we're going to stay in touch,' one girl said.

The leaving-drinks were perfunctory and she departed without a fanfare, but her words left their mark. You had to keep moving. Staying in one place for too long was a weakness.

The city meant driving into the office on weekends, exhausted, and feeling alone when the lights automatically dimmed after ten o'clock in the evening. It meant changing the dial of the air-conditioning because it always felt so cold inside that glass tower. Sometimes, the city just meant pressing my face against a window pane thirty-one floors above the rest of the world and looking out to the bottomless freedom of the night, longing so badly to go home.

My parents never really understood the city. Perhaps you had to work in it to fully understand.

As the months passed, the impasse grew wider, the gap more noticeable. When Ami and Papa came to visit, they complained that the city was too fast-paced for them.

'We can't keep up. You youngsters are always in such a rush!'

Feeling like foreigners in their own country, they gripped onto the railings of the moving runways in the underground as a stampede of humanity thundered past indifferently. Afterwards, they took pains to avoid travelling during rush hours when the area descended into a mass of pushing, shoving and hurrying limbs.

Bit by bit, I receded further into a world my family barely saw. The calls back home became less frequent. I lost track of my friends. As the hours in the office stretched even later, I would fall behind time and discover multiple missed calls on my phone. It would always be too late to call back. Everything fell out of turn and sync. I found myself perpetually trying to catch up on things. I missed engagements. I pulled out of things at the last minute. My calendar became a clutter of outstanding diary reminders. Sometimes it felt like I was running up the endless steps of a downward-moving escalator.

Slowly, I began to feel an emptiness. Despite being surrounded by throngs of people, the accelerated lifestyle was offset by moments of intense solitude. It was a barrenness that went beyond the vacuous materialism and surface covers. It grew inside. In the city, everything ran on currency and time, and at times I felt that I moved through money, not people. The city made me turn chameleon. I became French, I became Spanish, I became Italian, Greek, Turkish, Arab, Iranian, Afghani, Israeli. No one knew any better. But if I fitted in everywhere and could be anyone in the city, I was also nameless and no one in the city.

No one could place me. No one knew me. Day after day, people walked in and out of those glass doors, oblivious of one another. At times, I felt the city could make me disappear altogether and no one would notice. Away from home on those business trips abroad, I saw it most clearly. In those new-era metropolises, I witnessed a strange meeting-place of people from different parts who travelled and yet somehow never really mixed at all. It was a spoiled diversity. People came and went without any attachment to one another. I met so many people from across the globe, people of all sorts of partial and multiple and derivative identities. It seemed the more identities they had, the less attachment they held to anything. Relationships were fleeting and carefree, as if people were driven by some torturous desire to consume more to substantiate themselves, but like the story of Tantalus who stood up to his neck in water only for it to recede each time he stooped to drink, their thirst was insatiable. The city bred a tremendous loneliness. The more cities I visited, the more I became conscious of this peripatetic group. They seemed to have slipped through the borders, rootless, drifting along in a curious no-man's land with no sense of permanence, no sense of loyalty, no sense of home.

'All the homeless people in the world come here to die,' I once heard someone joke in a hotel lobby.

These cities had spawned a new vision of the world and at some level, it terrified me.

Periodically, Leila would call me from abroad. The speed of the city would not let me think of her for long, but when it paused, my thoughts always turned to her. I missed her. Growing up, we had been one and the same, indistinguishable, our experiences shared like our food and clothes.

'Stick together and no one will be able to break you,' Papa had told us as children as we sat tucked around him on his sofa and watched him take out a single toothpick and snap it. 'When you stick together, no one will be able to break you.' He

116

took a bundle of toothpicks and tried to snap it. The sticks did not break.

Since parting after graduation, my sister's course had taken a different trajectory, and she found herself swiftly rising through the ranks of a global marketing company with operations all over the world. In this new sector, she became quickly immersed in the experimental and innovative, in an industry that was operating at the very frontiers of this change. Suddenly plugged into the nucleus of modern technology and mass communication, she began tapping into unchartered terrain with an extraordinary access, travelling not just physically but also virtually across invisible wavelengths and high-speed networks to connect to more and more people and sell them new dreams. She had embraced the journey like a New World explorer.

'One of those modern girls,' my aunt remarked, almost spitting the words out like they had a bad taste.

But Leila's positioning at the precipice gave her an unnatural advantage, an uncanny foresight. Everything that was about to come, my sister saw it first. She packaged it. And then she sold it. She could sell diapers and pharmaceuticals to Africa. She could sell washing powder to China. Even mobile financial services to India. She was the future's poster-girl, its shining messenger, the forerunner, an advertising sensation. She made its vision sparkle like a trillion-cut diamond and sold a better brand of the world.

Caught up in the migrant lifestyle, Leila did not return home often, but in those scarce moments when we were together as a family and able to catch up, I would listen to her, captivated by her newfound zeal, as she sat around the dining table heralding the coming of a new age.

'All those billions of people living without access to information. Just imagine if they were plugged into this grid. Just imagine! It would revolutionise everything!'

117

Things were proliferating. The rest of the world was catching on, it was only a matter of time now. And at the dining table, she would grow more animated as she prophesied the changes that were unfolding, the discoveries being made, the patterns of growth, the access to markets, spinning around on her chair in excitement as she pointed to the various products around her in validation, dramatically reeling off continents.

'Even these coronations are from Africa, and these apricots,' she gestured pointing to the fruit basket, 'these apricots are from Asia! The very clothes you are wearing …'

She was McDonalds and Costa Coffee. She was Prada and Diet Coke. She was a universe of brands and labels: D&G, Gucci and Chanel. A happiness-making machine. The potential she had witnessed on her travels had triggered something and made her somehow more alive, more passionate, her smile broader, her lips somehow plumper as they opened and closed in excitement speaking of the coming construction sites, the factories, the plazas, the malls, the galleries, the towering high-rises with their purple carpets and abstract furniture.

And yet, like all grand prospects, my sister was perpetually out of reach. The great expectation to which she was wed soon carried her off, never letting her linger at home for long. She followed a constant monitor of currency and digital signals. The tide of technology-exchange was just the beginning. New markets were emerging. Opportunities were growing. Demand was increasing. Communication proliferating. There were infinite possibilities. Whatever the trail of devastation, whatever the destruction that followed, there was no looking back. It was necessary to design better, build taller, produce more, sell quicker.

'There's so much to do and never enough time, and if you slow down, you'll get left behind.'

It was Leila's constant warning, her greatest fear. The fear of being left behind. It did not matter if the rundown was cast aside or the old discarded. Change and transition were inevitable parts of this transformation, part of survival. And as she became more convinced of her vision, those perfect cherry-gloss lips would take in continents, consume them, swallow without savouring, talk faster, become more passionate, more compelling.

This dream was a new part of her family. Her loyalty to me and that ideal were on a par. I had no greater claim, not because I meant any less, but because that was what it meant to be part of an interconnected, organic world. She was at the Rubicon, breaking down boundaries, ploughing forward like an express shuttle, crossing into new realms, pushing imaginative capacity further into the horizon. I felt she was so far ahead.

Oh, my sister, she was so sure, so confident, so beautiful when she spoke of her vision! I instantly wanted to be like her. I wanted to be just as assured of the future she spoke of, and the promises it offered. She ran towards it like a bird with outstretched wings. I envied the freedom she felt as she moved between cities like water. She was fearless, a fountain of change. I wanted to join her, to follow her in that chase towards the sun, but in spite of everything, I found myself perpetually glancing backwards. I could not help it. I clung to the old.

Although I could not fully bend to it, I understood the lure that had taken my sister. It was undeniable. There was an uncanny freedom that came with being a stranger. In the cities, you were neither here nor there and you found yourself slipping in and out almost intuitively. With all the travelling, there was an expectation that you were always away and so it became possible to move in and out of attachments without the guilt or the responsibility of commitment you suffered when permanently tied to one place.

People seemed to open up more freely when they knew they were about to disappear. Those cities became surrogate homes. At some level, everyone was away from something, and, in a place where nobody belongs, I suppose, after a while it starts to feel like home.

As time passed, I began to wonder whether this was the direction the world was heading. Was the old world really disappearing? As I moved in and out of airport terminals half-guessing where the people around me were travelling, I wondered whether the names of those flashing cities meant something less than they did before. What did these destinations mean now? They were no longer the end points they once were. Some of them, after all, had been nothing before. Dismantled docks or just desert tracts. And what was a home anyway in a place where you could pull back the land from the sea and create new worlds out of nothing?

Somewhere in the midst of it all, I had seen something that made me pause. I had encountered a strange middle space. It was the same in every city, all over the world. There were moments when everything slowed down and I had witnessed the walkways and underpasses tranquil and peopleless. In London, they were typically at four or five in the morning when the whole office floor was empty and a momentary lull in activity allowed me to pick up a couple hours of rest. The office had sleeping pods for overnight workers but I could never switch off. My desk was on the thirty-first floor and I would take off my heels and wander across the floor to the glass windows on the adjacent side. From that part of the building I could see the whole of the city emerging from the early morning mist.

London was never more beautiful than in those moments. In the half-light, the city changed colours and I saw the face of my birthplace without makeup. Just before dawn, the same scene played out over and again striking a chord deep inside: the parting of that white foam, the great yoke breaking over, the pale golden fingertips descending through the haze. Sachets of light in the mist. The sight was so natural, so constant and I would always think there was something so overwhelming about it. It was the same no matter where I went. At daybreak, the world took my breath away, and in those moments I became a child again, playing at the back of our garden with no one else around, thinking how large and wonderful the outdoors had seemed from that small enclosure, full of strange and extraordinary things. It was as if in those moments the spirit of the city reached out to comfort me. Each time I looked out into that dawn, I saw reflected back at me the traces of something deeper and greater that had not been relinquished, something innate that not only made a better world possible, but was proof that such a world was already alive and gently waking. As a softness tempered the features of the city, the harshness of all that took place during the day subsided into a daily ritual of self-balancing. From those glass windows, I looked out and an irrepressible sense of hope and possibility would fill me, and I would be touched by the thought that perhaps, from different windows, someone else might be watching a similar scene and thinking the same thing. At five o'clock the lifts beeped open and the cleaners made their entrance with buckets and mops, and with that cue I would turn from the window and walk reluctantly back to work.

Perhaps then, in some strange way, it made sense that it was against a backdrop of London's shifting skylines and histories, amongst the conveyer belt of different people entering and exiting from all across the world that my path locked and knotted with someone who filled my longing for a resting place. Someone on whom I pinned my hopes of growing that other world with. In a strange way, I suppose it was only fair and right that it was in the heart of the city that I met Morad.

Morad, born of a hyphenated, splintered identity like mine, a rock in a current of change. Morad, who seemed everything I was and more, only that his secret garden was different from mine.

121

Before I met Morad, I knew nothing of Bangladesh. At school, the Asian kids I'd known had been of either Indian or Pakistani descent and so I was surprised, if not a little embarrassed, to discover that all this time I had been living next-door to a community of people that hailed from an entirely separate part of the Indian subcontinent, a place I knew virtually nothing about.

Morad had grown up just outside London in one of a neat row of terraced homes that ran identically like dominos all the way down to the end of the road. Without knowing it, I had spent my childhood less than a few miles away from him, sharing the same bus-stops and landmarks and even some of the same distant acquaintances.

'Old Station Road,' he offered helpfully. 'I guess it's because it's behind the station.'

His dark eyes smiled down at me in a way that triggered a strange sensation inside. Those eyes, they were the first things that took me in, so wide and deep like wells of warmth. We conversed in mounting intrigue, hurtling through our early years of growing up so near to one another, mapping out the mutual milestones and turning points.

'Alderton Hill?' he laughed. 'Of course I know it. It's the road with all the big gardens. Always wondered what it was like growing up in one of those houses.'

Those big eyes peered down into mine again taking me into their compass, and growing wider in curiosity. Morad still lived in the area, and as he spoke of the familiar spots in my old neighbourhood, my head began to fill with a flurry of buried memories, like how I always ran up Alderton Hill to post my father's bills in the red letterbox perched at the top of the slope (and how that hill always seemed like Everest when I was small), or how lovely it felt squelching across the lawn in the morning, treading on the moist grass when I carried my racquets to the back of the garden. The tennis centre was still there. Slowly, the city shrank into something cosily familiar. Yet the more I got to

122

know of Morad, the more I found my eyes opening to a side of London I never knew existed, and I caught the sense of something rich, something full.

Although he grew up on the outskirts of London only minutes away from our hill, the area where he lived was a young multi-cultural belt quite unlike our aging white-haired neighbourhood. Many of his neighbours were also Bengali, with young families of their own, and throughout the day friends would wander in and out of his parents' home for tea and chatter. Their children came too, and when the other boys arrived, they would race upstairs to play games in the attic. From the outset, the diaspora in the vicinity had been organised and proactive. As it grew, societies were set up and committees inaugurated, and it did not take long before the locality developed into a strong, communal hub.

For Morad, I soon realised that ever since childhood his life had been inextricably linked to the life of this hidden community. He spoke of it like an adoptive parent. It had been there for as long as he could remember. Everyone was an uncle, an aunt, an older brother, grandfather or grandmother. And above all, everything tied back to Bangladesh. Growing up, children learnt Bengali and got to know the villages their parents came from. Place names were reference points and families would always ask, so the kids would learn the names of abstract districts and hamlets in Bangladesh, sometimes without ever having visited them.

Every few months or so, a fresh influx of families would move into the area injecting a stronger presence of Bangladesh into the community, and Morad and the other children would learn the latest games and swear words and phrases as if they were growing up in villages halfway across the world. The presence of that homeland was ubiquitous. At cultural days, the children got together and sang local folk songs and celebrated Independence Day, the anniversary of the Nobel poet laureate

Rabindranath Tagore and all the other important national days in the Bengali calendar. His sisters would dress up in pretty pink saris, and wear waterlilies in their hair, and each time they went onto the dais to sing, he would accompany them, beating his fingers rhythmically on a small wooden *tabla*.

On our first evening together, Morad opened the door of his car and took me into the heart of the city. The car was an old, faded, gold hatchback with a look of timelessness about it. It creaked as the door opened, and as soon as I sunk into the worn passenger seat, I felt as if I had been placed there for perpetuity.

'It's a special night,' Morad smiled.

There was something he wanted to show me, and we raced past the white stone lions standing guard on the city's pillars, past the bronze statues watching on the pavement, taking bends and detours as we followed the streetlamps that slinked around the river, joining up the beams of light with our own excitement. The current cast a golden ripple of glitter across the water, and under the moonlight I caught sight of a couple kissing by the embankment. Their silhouettes quivered. I remember it like yesterday. The city seemed vast that night, so fresh and full of possibility. In the darkness, I saw a side to London that I had never seen before, layered with colour and emotion. As we passed several oppressive-looking council estates, for the first time I noticed small details, like how the hard and cold exteriors were softened by a miscellany of brightly-patterned materials hanging on the looping washing lines to dry. In the faint outdoor light, several heavily-clad women shuffled in and out amongst a cluster of evergreen pot plants. Though I could not see their faces, I noticed that their veils were beautifully textured and I wondered who they were. Where did they come from? It never occurred to me they might have been born in the same part of the world as me.

We took a turning and all at once the faint smell of spice filled the car and I recognised the East End curry houses, the counters over-spilling with their eternal *gelabis*. Morad looked over to me, his eyes drawing me into their orbit as he shifted gear and we turned again, passing through more estates. Pockets of Asian youths loitered about, slouched against walls, smoked as they sat on steps, and I became increasingly conscious that the whole area was brimming with youngsters. It was cold outside and I wondered what they were doing on the streets so late at night. There was so much life in the dark, the city seemed wide awake. By the entrance to an estate, a group of boys laughed and cracked jokes. One started to mock-fight with another. Their dark clothes merged with the colour of the night, but against the blackness their trainers shone out in luminosity. As they played in the shadows, it looked as if their bodies were dancing. At the next turning I was taken aback, shocked to see a street-name loom up in the window written in Bengali script. Another followed. The translations were written too. *Fournier Street. Buxton Street.*

My thoughts called out to the night. What an incredible city! How had I failed to notice these things before?

At the mouth of Brick Lane, Morad pulled over to pick up a snack from a midnight bakery. It was the first time I had walked along Brick Lane and the street was bustling, teeming with late-night revellers. A long queue snaked around the entrance to a Bagel shop and I could not help thinking there was something curious about seeing an old Jewish bakery nestled amongst a crowd of curry houses and *sari* stores. All along the street, young Asian boys with short crew cuts and colourful trainers stood in the doorways touting for business.

'Best curry on Brick Lane! Best curry!'

'Beer, yes! Come here for beer!'

They wore their pants low below the waist and smoked in public. One of the boys wolf-whistled as I passed then made some remark in a language I did not understand.

'*Oh shundori orkhanor ow!*'

Morad shot him a fierce look and the boy turned away.

We returned to the car with our bagels.

When we finally arrived at the park, Morad stopped the car and got out. He pointed across the lawn to an unusual looking red and white monument. I must have driven past the park countless times before and never noticed it.

'It's the *Shaheed Minar*, the Martyr Monument,' he told me, smiling gently, and explained it was an imitation of a much larger monument in Dhaka, the capital of Bangladesh.

I walked up to the monument. There were five white rectangular columns propped up on a brick-red raised platform. The middle column was slightly taller than the rest. A large crimson disc lay in the centre behind them.

'Do you know what this is?' He moved closer and ran his fingers against the backdrop of a blood-red rising sun. 'It's a symbol of a mother protecting her sons. At midnight every year on this day, people come to this park to remember.'

The date marked a sombre historical moment. Just over fifty years ago, a group of Bengali students were shot in Dhaka as they campaigned to protect their mother tongue. The atrocity proved a catalyst in the liberation war against Pakistan, finally resulting in the birth of Bangladesh, and in recognition of the event UNESCO commemorated the date as International Mother Language Day.

'Bangladesh,' Morad declared with a hint of pride, 'is the only country to have gone to war over the right to speak its own language. It's important to know your mother tongue,' he added half-chidingly, knowing I did not know mine. 'It's what keeps you connected to back home.'

I listened quietly, letting the comment pass.

I was surprised to see metal barriers and police vans along the entranceway to the park. It was still too early in the evening and the area was relatively empty. I imagined a large congregation gathering at midnight. Morad moved closer to me and took my hand. He pulled me gently towards him. In the cold, I felt the warmth of his body against mine. For several minutes, we stood there in silence, looking out at that monument. A number of people trickled in through the gates. I grew inquisitive and pointed towards them, wanting to stay on. But Morad seemed reluctant. He glanced over his shoulder more than once, as if worried. We left soon afterwards. I guess that was our first date.

Still, the colour and vibrancy of his community gripped me and I was excited to know more. Each time we met, Morad would tell me something new, reeling me in a little more. Through his stories, without ever meeting them, I gained a strong sense of the different characters and personalities within his community, the various aunts and uncles, which neighbours were nice and which were not, the excesses of certain youngsters and why it was necessary to be careful of one nosy old aunty who lived just around the corner and was always snooping for gossip.

Often, he called in between ferrying his parents from one social gathering to the next and in this way, I learnt about the weekly Town Hall lunches, the regular community excursions, the weddings and of course the annual coach-trip. The first time he described the coach-trip, I listened in quiet fascination. The trip took place each year and all the parents looked forward to it with a childlike eagerness. One of the families volunteered to prepare packed-lunches for the journey, and as the bus made its way through different parts of Europe, *samosas, shami kebabs* and crispy fish snacks would be passed from seat to seat. There was always some drama on the trip. Somebody would forget something. Somebody would be late. Somebody would get lost. The coach would break down.

'You could offer them Versailles Palace, but it would mean nothing to them,' he joked. 'Sometimes I think they go on those trips just to look forward to coming home.'

Morad used to accompany his parents on the trips when

he was young, but after joining the city, he stopped going. Instead, he would drop his parents off at the station and wave them goodbye. The other kids that worked in the city did the same thing too. I tried to imagine what it must have been like. It was so different from anything I had known in Alderton Hill and I chuckled quietly at the thought of sixty Bengali elders tucking into curry and rice on the steps of Montmartre or wandering through the piazzas of Rome. It sounded funny and strange, although oddly appealing at the same time.

In truth, I was fascinated by Morad. I was fascinated by his stories and the things he told me. Throbbing through him, I saw a homeland that I felt I had lost when I was growing up. Soft was his love for that place, soft and tender. Those dark globes drew me in, inviting me to gaze upon another world. That world was alive and vibrant, not phantasmagoric and fragmented like mine. Somehow it had embedded in the city of my birth, threading its own fabric into a tapestry that I was starting to realise was far more nuanced than the one I had previously known. It had survived without being consumed or lost. It had endured. Deep inside, I was excited by the prospect of sharing in this new discovery with Morad. I would listen quietly at the way he waxed lyrical about Bangladesh and be reminded of my own love for an incomprehensible, faraway place.

He seemed to know so much about his motherland, it amazed me. And each time he spoke of it, his face would soften and he would suddenly become somehow more vulnerable, somehow more beautiful in my eyes, speaking of it so full of love and tenderness and pride, as if somehow a part of that land had broken off and he now carried that small island with him.

Never before had I met someone so assured of his heritage and his connection to it. It hung in his heart, closer than his aortic valve, shielded and hidden from view. Perhaps, like me, he feared others would not understand. Perhaps because, deep down, he always knew it was his Achilles heel. But if my heart

128

was called to testify, it would say it was in those moments that I grew to love him, for it was always then that I saw most clearly the traces of my own story written all over him.

In the loneliness of those long hours in the city, amidst coffee cups and midnight phone calls, our friendship deepened. Little by little I fell in love. My happiness grew on his. My joy flowed from his. Time passed in the office without me feeling it. As our phone conversations rolled later into the night eating into the darkness and the first traces of light began to touch the sky, I would fall asleep to the sound of his breathing, imagining his soft presence still beside me.

But Morad came and went, and each time he left for Bangladesh I missed him, and in his absence the city would grow cold again. He would be gone for days. Several weeks would feel like several months.

When he was young, he would return to Bangladesh only sporadically as his parents could not afford the regular trips back, and between those initial visits there had been long, extended breaks. He was seven years old the first time he went back and his relatives had flocked around in welcome, assuming he was living the life of a king in England. At that time, everything in Bangladesh seemed cheap and polished — the scooters, the clothes, the food, the toys, the enormous shiny billboards — but it also seemed a stressful place. In the streets, peddlers heckled and his father cautioned him to walk close to his sisters like a shield. People harangued his parents for money and in the evenings through the walls he would listen to the voices of the spiralling guilt complexes that accompanied his parents' pressure of supporting poor relatives and younger cousins back in their village. Everyone wanted a way into England, and believed his family to be their great hope. His parents made excuses. No one was able to understand how difficult it had been raising a young family abroad. Morad could not afford to go on school trips like the other children in his class. He could not buy the toys and games his friends took for granted. In the evenings while his friends were playing after school activities, he worked for a local shopkeeper washing vegetables in the backroom to earn his pocket-money. But for the sake of keeping up appearances his parents did not tell anyone.

When relatives complained of the time that passed between their visits, his father only apologised quietly, too ashamed to make it known it had taken all those years to save enough money for that trip. For them, England was a shiny poster destination, as fortuitous as a golden lottery ticket.

'*Amrar by Londoni!*' (our brother is from London!), they gloated proudly to their friends.

It made all their hopes possible, their hardships more bearable. Before leaving the village, Morad bought a bag of candy and shared the sweets with his younger cousins. Their faces broke into enormous smiles and, though it emptied his pocket at the time, he left the place feeling a little happier.

Now, though, he returned to Bangladesh every year. He took leave from work in large chunks, saving up the days all year round. When he went, he would be gone for several weeks.

Travelling on business only made our time apart longer. He did not call often while he was away and when the calls came they were brief and guarded. Nothing like our midnight conversations that stole into the morning hours. We rushed through trivialities — how things were, the family, the weather — and then he was gone. If I was lucky, sometimes I received an email. I looked forward to the days they came. The messages were short, spotted with complaints about second-rate internet connections and unfathomable keyboards, and each time I read them I would sigh, wondering if he missed me too and longing to hear a little more.

One morning a brown envelope arrived in my letterbox.

It contained four folded scraps of notepaper scribbled with black ink. When I realised where they came from, my heart skipped a beat. There was something wonderful about receiving the crumpled, physical pages and seeing the untidy handwriting. Morad had written the letters during an eight-hour train journey. I followed his travels through the loops and arcs of his handwriting. The letter began tidily, with neat cordialities, updating me on generalities; where he was, who he was with and so on. But as the writing continued and the flow of thought became more disjointed, the script became larger and messier. At times the writing spiralled out of control into peripatetic digressions, breaking into nuggets of random childlike wonder.

The sky is full of silver dots. I think the crickets are doing choir practice all around me, he wrote.

His writing touched me with its simplicity, and through the words I felt his excitement and joy at being in the heart of a different world. A blob of ink smudged halfway across the page. Perhaps the carriage jolted or maybe something outside distracted him for the writing trailed off mid-sentence.

I closed my eyes, picturing where he may have been. It was a quiet star-studded night and I saw a train moving in the dark, crossing through vast stretches of fertile farmland. I imagined the rest of his family nodding up and down in sleep as the wheels chugged along on the tracks, and I saw a little wide-eyed boy looking out of the window, smiling to himself.

We're in a small fishing town, the letter picked up again and I knew then that he had reached his mother's village.

He had spoken to me of it before and I imagined him out there busying himself amongst the pastoral scenes. The writing continued describing the nine-mile trek to the nearest internet booth only to discover the connection was down.

It was why I couldn't email, he explained apologetically.

Life was pared back to basics there, so unlike the frenetic pace of London. The homes were stark and modest, but the children were always smiling. A gaggle of younger cousins constantly surrounded him.

At night, they tuck themselves around me in my bed. I've made the most of it by getting them to take it in turns to give me head massages.

I laughed out loud when I read this, imagining him smiling at his resourcefulness. He had even bought them a bar of soap to make sure they washed their hands properly beforehand.

It makes them happy, he joked and went on to describe how his little cousins competed with one another for their place in the queue.

I knew how fond he was of those head massages. It reminded me of the times when I ran my hands through his hair and softly kneaded his temples. When my fingers touched his brow, he would instinctively grow passive and sleepy, soft and pliable like putty in my palms. He fell asleep so quickly and as soon as he did, I would stop and watch him lying there peacefully, often feeling a little envious. Sometimes, one brown eye opened and looked up at me confused, as if seeking reassurance and I would stroke his hair, soothing him gently, until he drifted off again.

But at times, I could not deter an overwhelming sense that Morad was watching me. Those deep brown eyes followed me everywhere. I could not shake off their stare. It was a feeling I had for the first year of our being together. I felt under constant surveillance like someone was quietly watching, observing, assessing and monitoring. Often I'd be caught up absorbed in something and turn to find Morad staring at me quietly, deep in thought.

'You're different,' he once reflected and I began to realise there was something about me that bothered him.

At the beginning, when he spoke of his community functions, I offered to join him, keen to share in the source of his happiness. They were never too far away. I must have asked three or four times before I eventually gave up. He never took me.

Over time, I realised the absence of that reciprocity was not an accidental oversight. All that time, Morad had been wary about something, though what it was I was not quite sure. Sometimes, he asked me things that surprised me.

'Why haven't you been taught Kashmiri?'

'Why don't you wear traditional clothes at home?'

'Why don't you live with your parents?'

I tried to explain, telling him about my early years, about Alderton Hill, the leafy driveways, the roads full of cherry blossom, the duck ponds and the tennis courts. I told him about Cambridge and its perfectly symmetrical quads, about my move to the city and my travels across the world and of course I told him about Kashmir. But it never seemed enough.

I was not sure what I represented to Morad. Somehow, in his eyes, I did not fit. Whatever expectation he had of me, it seemed at odds with my reality. My white skin seemed to fascinate him. It was somehow aberrant, something he had not envisaged from a person of my background. It did not conform to his idea of what he thought I should have been. Sometimes he would stare into my eyes, analysing the small amber flecks in my irises.

'It's like green with bits of gold in it,' he murmured once, bending in closer and staring harder, only seconds later to retreat far away.

Each time he pulled away, it was as if the whole of him withdrew from me also, returning to some unreachable place I could never follow.

'But I don't understand, Liyana. You're *Asian*. How can you be so white?'

And those large dark eyes would peer into mine as he pulled his face closer again searching for something that was not there.

One day, I will give back something to this place, the letter

133

continued.

And I remembered the first time he told me of his parents' initial experiences in England, and how his voice had dropped as he spoke softly and quietly, almost murmuring the tales like a sad lullaby. His father had grown up in Dhaka, the capital city of Bangladesh, and was one of five brothers. He had been a reasonably educated man and there was very little about his life that stuck out, except that he fell in love with a girl from a fishing village who was almost twenty years his junior. Not long after they married, they moved to England. His father initially came over to treat a speech impediment suffered since birth and it had never been his intention to stay. But like many other Bengalis at that time, even without the chance of a cure, he stayed on longer than expected and settled in London. The rest of his brothers remained in Bangladesh.

At the start, his father tried his hand at many jobs but found his prospects set back by his limited English and the latent hostility of that time. The first time he visited a local barber he was curtly instructed to read the sign outside.

NO COLOUREDS!

In other parts of the city, the resentment was far worse and many Bengalis found themselves openly subjected to racist attacks from bigoted gangs. Windows were smashed. Bricks were hurled and excrement smeared into letterboxes. The women stopped venturing out alone and certain areas were marked as no-go zones by community elders. But sick of the tirades and fear, some of the youngsters decided to band together and formed groups to protect their communities. Many learnt self-defence. On some estates there were confrontations as resistance gradually overturned passive resignation.

Eventually, his father was helped by a friend who procured a job at the Pakistan embassy, and it was there that he worked as a clerk deciding who may and who may not enter the country with the seal of a red rubber stamp, until 1971 when

Bangladesh declared its independence from Pakistan. On the day the news was announced, he, along with a large contingent of fellow Bengalis, handed in their resignations en masse and left.

While Morad's father was away at the embassy, his mother worked fifteen-hour shifts at home as a seamstress. She would spend the whole day hunched over her sewing machine, juggling a pile of tailoring with caring for her young children, unable to leave the home. When his sisters were old enough, they helped with whatever chores they could. Although his mother looked back and made light of the ordeal, I could tell that the experience had left its imprint on Morad, for each time I listened to him, I felt him re-inhabiting his parents' hardship and sensed through him their longing for the way of life they left behind.

The community that grew up in the area had thrived out of marginalisation, replicating the cherished and familiar ways back home, and I soon realised Morad's love for Bangladesh was deeply connected to the love of his own parents. A sense of pining permeated everything that attached to that place. Small trinkets, jewellery, books, cooking … anything that elicited a memory and kept that old world alive suddenly assumed vast import. His father was a quiet man, made even shyer by his stammer, but his love of Bengali art was especially poignant. He would spend much of his retired life in private painting, or reading Bengali newspapers, or simply whiling away the time watching old arty Bengali movies. Often he sat for hours in their living room thumbing through the poetry of Bengali writers like Bharat Chandra Iswar Gupta, Biharilal Chakraborti, Rabindranath Tagore, Kazi Nazrul Islam and Jatindramohan Bagchi.

'Sometimes,' Morad told me laughing, 'he just sits there smiling and singing the melodies to himself.'

Although England did not prove the panacea for his stammer, somehow in those moments when he was singing alone, the ailment simply disappeared.

The last page of the letter was folded messily and torn in one corner. I turned it over, not wanting it to end.

How do I solve a problem like you, Liyana?

It had taken some time before Morad told me his parents wanted him to marry a Bengali girl. I was not Bengali. It seemed, in some way, I was different from all the other Asians he'd grown up with. I represented something new, something that didn't fit into their vision of the world. And yet despite this, he confessed, there was something about me that was so intensely familiar. He had never felt as comfortable with anyone else before. He had never felt so at home. And I remember how one day in my apartment, he had surprised me, coming up from behind as I was putting on my make-up in front of the mirror. At first, I did not notice him and when I saw him staring at me, I suddenly felt exposed. I stopped what I was doing and watched as he put his arms around my waist and surveyed our reflection in the mirror contemplatively. All at once, he seemed to melt, bending forward to rest his head against my shoulder and speaking to me penitently, like someone who had erred and lost his way.

'You weren't meant to happen, Liyana,' he said with a sigh. 'You slipped in under the radar and somehow despite my attempts you're still here.'

The same words were splayed in the letter and I heard him whispering them to me again. There had been genuine concern in his voice when he said them. But his softness dissipated all doubt. He had held me closely for a moment, his eyes lost in thought, and I watched him smile to himself in the glass, before finally letting me go and walking from the room.

I'm not going to read over what I've written because I'll probably end up crossing it out, the last lines of the letter concluded. *I suppose the point I'm trying to make is I miss you, Liyana. I miss you so much and I can't wait to come home.*

Late one evening, not long after he returned from Bangladesh, the clocks turned back an hour and time stood still. On my balcony, against the city's red skyline, Morad looked into my eyes and whispered. 'I want to marry you.'

He repeated the words three times like a spell, locking me in his gaze and refusing to let me go. I stood there, dazed, half-paralysed, and felt a glow inside each time he said so. As he held me in his arms and his eyes bore down on me, a part of me hesitated, half-afraid that he might waver a little or return to that far off place to which he would often retreat. But this time, he did not. That night, he held me tightly in his embrace, those dark brown eyes pledging their constancy to me, closing only to open once more and flood me with their faith like the tide. He smiled, as if reading my thoughts, and bent down to kiss me on the forehead, and for the first time, I felt complete.

When we returned indoors, Morad told me about his trip to Bangladesh.

'I can't wait to take you,' he murmured, taking me into his arms and stroking my hair tenderly.

I nodded happily, quietly thinking of my own longing to show him the Valley, and when he finished recounting all his adventures, I laid in his lap daydreaming idly, telling him about Kashmir.

Within the walls of the lake city, there was a beautiful palace that once belonged to the Maharaja and during the better times, it had been converted into a luxury hotel. People congregated there from all over the world: film stars, celebrities, diplomats, the rich and famous, travellers of every ilk and kind. But when the troubles came to the Valley, they all fled, leaving the rooms and hallways empty and the palace forsaken, like some enchanted castle under curse waiting for its rightful king to return. A walled pathway wound around a slope leading up to the palace and all along the route blood-red roses, hundreds of them, hung over the tall, ivy-draped walls. It was like a secret garden.

As you drove up, you would see them spilling out over the pillars in abundance. At the very top, the doors of the palace stood perpetually open, and rolling out before them like a gigantic magic carpet the most magnificent lawns lay in wait offering panoramic views of the entire lake city.

The first time I entered the palace gardens, there were no other visitors around. It was so quiet, even the hotel staff seemed made of tin and lace. The garden hung suspended above the city, and from the heights, I could see out for miles. As the sun beat down and melted over the landscape mineralising everything around me, I found myself sheened in a bronze light looking out as thousands of copper, gold and silver roofs flared in the distance, shining like shifting aluminium foil. The sun turned pink. In one eyeful, it felt as if I was taking in all the precious metals of the earth. The world lay spread before me in all its sparkling beauty, ripe and ready for the taking. It took my breath away. Each time I returned to the palace, I waited for that moment at sunset and the same thoughts overcame me. How could all the complexities of the world not give way in that instant? How could everything wrong not simply resolve and melt in that perfection? And I would stand alone on those unpeopled lawns, looking out over a desolate kingdom longing to share that moment as the city stretched before me throwing my loneliness back like a mirror.

Whenever I spoke to Morad of Kashmir, it was always that very moment I wanted to give him. I wanted him to be there standing next to me. And though he insisted on plotting out our lives on flawed maps in secret behind closed doors, it was always that open and inviting vision I kept returning to and ached to make him know.

'Perhaps one day we will marry there,' I told him dreamily as he caressed my hair. 'One day we will go there,' I repeated softly.

Perhaps, I thought, we would say our vows beneath the

ancient chinar tree in the garden where Gandhi once sat and the smoky fragrance of *isband* would fill the air. No expense would be spared. We would have the best of everything there and if it could not be brought from Kashmir, we would bring it from England. Whatever we wanted … everything was possible.

I continued helplessly, drifting into imagination. Perhaps, we would celebrate on the lake just as I had always envisaged it. We would unmoor one of the huge houseboats, have it dripping with fairy-lights and lanterns, and drift through the lotus gardens. The lights would make the inky waters sparkle with hundreds and thousands of jewels as our boat lapped across the ripples.

On the banks on the other side, I could see them all, clear and real as they had been. They were waiting for us. I could picture it perfectly. White marquees billowed on the lawns and a man danced in flowing skirts and anklets as, one by one, my cousins appeared out of the darkness carrying candles in brightly decorated henna bowls. Their faces were still the same. They had not changed. Somewhere in the night, that musty paste would be smeared onto my palms and when eventually we left to return to the palace once more, they would throw soft confetti over us and sing like the old times. The boatmen knew me well. It would not be difficult to hire a *shikara* to ferry us back to the other side.

Morad kissed me gently on the forehead, not having the heart to stop me as I let my dreams flow lucidly like water before him.

I was missing Kashmir. It had been almost three years since my return. Morad's trips back to Bangladesh only intensified my longing to go back. But while his route back was accessible and familiar, a road well-trodden, my own path had crumbled away once again and with it my hopes of returning to the Valley.

Since the attacks in India everything had changed, and I

139

found myself encountering difficulties with my visa. On the application form, I was required to declare my parents' birthplace, but after completing the sections and submitting the paperwork, a lady behind the counter took out a red marker pen and drew a thick circle over where I had written Pakistan as my mother's birthplace. My application was immediately put to one side. With that red circle a wall was drawn around me. It was as if with one stroke my British passport became inconsequential. I had been marked as something else, and whatever it was, it now imperilled my right to return.

What followed was a humiliating routine. I was summoned to the High Commission for an interview and two men sat in front of me asking strange, arbitrary questions. It felt like an interrogation. They asked the same questions again and again, in so many varying ways, as if hoping for a different answer. But like a broken record, I kept repeating the same explanation.

'My family comes from the Valley.'

I told them what I knew of my parents' and grandparents' stories just as they had been told to me. The men cross-examined the histories and migrations, delving into an undocumented past, demanding clarifications and explanations.

'When did this happen?'
'When did that happen?'
'Why did that happen?'
'Why didn't that happen?'
'This bit doesn't make sense.'
'That date must have come before.'
'But what is the *real* reason?'
'What is the *real* reason you want to go to Kashmir?'

I tried to fill in the gaps as best I could but at times I had no answer, and each time I faltered the two men looked at one another as if somehow I had just confirmed whatever suspicions they held. My accounts were never enough. There were blanks, spaces, inconsistencies, things they told me I got wrong. But I was no omniscient historian, not privy to all the past. All I knew were the stories that had been passed to me. The people that might have been able to fill the blanks were no longer there. But my interviewers were stone-faced and aloof, and sitting in that room trying to convince them, I became disheartened. As the Valley receded further from my grasp, it grew somehow even more rarefied, somehow even more sacred.

News from the Valley drip-fed back to London. Things had soured in Kashmir. The same technology Leila had lionised in her dining table sermons was now the only thing that kept the Valley alive for me, for with each piece of news that came from that part of the world, I felt the reverberations back in England. I searched online and found openings, writings, postings and blogs, photographs and amateur videos that had been shared, each one a missive of resistance that broke the wall of silence.

As time passed, the reports of skirmishes and incidents increased. There were rumours of strikes. A sea of emerald flags filling the streets. An old shrine besieged and destroyed. The school where Leila and I played basketball was set alight.

One of the boys emailed us. *All that remains of our school is a pile of ashes and burnt memories. Pray for us, Ma'am.*

It was just the beginning.

Shots were fired in the inner city. It was reported an elderly grandfather was among the dead. He had been returning from Khanqah-e-Moula shrine. The article contained a picture of an old man wearing round thick-rimmed glasses and made me think of the *shawl-wallah's* father. An unremitting period of curfew followed, with small children wetting their beds at night. The city dogs grew fiercer, stalking the streets in packs. My uncle walked up and down his gated driveway day after day. Some of the elder kids started climbing walls, sneaking out in the dead of night to find milk and bread. Some pelted stones.

The Valley's English medium local newspaper reported

141

that hundreds of thousands of youngsters had gathered in the inner city.

> *'Zor se bolo – azaadi!*
> *Zara haath bajaake – azaadi!*
> *wo aayi – azaadi!*
> *wo phoolon waali – azaadi!*
> *wo mehki mehki- azaadi!*
> *wo pyaari pyaari –azaadi!!*
> *wo jaan se pyaari – azaadi!*
> *gaddaro sunlo – azaadi!*
> *makkaro sunlo – azaadi!'*

> ('Shout aloud – Freedom!
> Clap your hands – Freedom!
> There it comes – Freedom!
> Flowery Freedom!
> Fragrant Freedom!!
> Beautiful freedom!
> Dearer than life – Freedom!
> Listen Traitors – Freedom!
> Listen Hypocrites – Freedom!')

I read about it as I scoured the internet a million miles away and pictured my basketball boys racing forward among them as the bodies of a hundred youths pitched out and collapsed lifeless in the laps of their mothers.

Shaheed Mudasir Basheer, martyred in Sopore 2 hours back. Sopore loses 1 more football player.

The news spread online like wildfire as SMS services were banned. There were crack-downs on social networking sites. Teenagers were arrested and taken away. I stopped receiving emails. Communication regressed to letters as the Valley was pushed further back in time. Fewer and fewer words trickled

142

back to England as a black veil was thrown over the lake city engulfing it in amnesiac darkness. Suddenly everything about that place seemed perishable.

When will it all end? Even paper seemed to be running out for the words were scribbled over a map of Kashmir in blood-red ink, a final plea for help. It was the last message I received from the boys in my basketball team as one by one all the schools closed down.

A year passed, two years passed, and still I was unable to go back. But deep down, I knew I had to. At some level I knew there was an importance to those travels that went beyond me: my bond, however small, broke a barrier. It was a responsibility I had somehow inherited. I had to keep that path back open, I had to keep that door ajar. The cords of our connection, though strained and tested, compelled me to keep trying. I gathered supplementary documentation. I contacted the National Archives for naturalisation certificates. I appealed for letters of support from my local Member of Parliament. I even tried tracking down death certificates, imploring Ami and Papa to post me any evidence that might prove a link, a connection, a proof of presence or footprint, anything at all. But the whole process drove me to the brink of tears and at one point, I sobbed down the phone to the visa officer in frustration. It hurt knowing my English friends could get the same visa over the counter in a day or two without any fuss. I had been born in England like them. It made me feel somehow different, somehow less British.

Only my father was able to procure a visa to return, and each time he came home, he brought back missives from the city of invisible siege. But on the third trip out to the Valley alone, even he became downcast. My mother and sister had struggled to obtain visas too.

'Surely, *surely* it must be a human rights' violation to keep you from your roots,' my father murmured unhappily down the phone. The line was crackly and the interference choked him.

Electricity black-outs had grown more frequent. As I sat beside my mother at the dining room table, trying to decipher the words filtering through the receiver from thousands of miles away, I wondered why it had to be so difficult. Each day my father rang twice from the Valley, once in the morning and once in the evening, and I could tell he was homesick.

Just days before my twenty-eighth birthday, I received an envelope in the post containing my passport. It was returned without a visa, and only a slip that read: *Case referred to Competent Authority, HC Delhi.*

I was distraught and immediately tried to contact the High Commission. The officer dealing with my case informed me that I was required to submit a list of all the countries I had visited in the past ten years before progressing any further with my application. In despair, I thought of all the places I had flown to during the past ten years and stared down at that slip of paper, feeling utterly helpless. I felt trapped. The coils of bureaucracy were never-ending. Tears of frustration collected at the back of my eyes. How could I convince them? How could I make them understand?

I took out a pad of paper and a pen and, determined, I began the list, writing down the countries, one after another.

I had flown across Europe, stood suspended above the vast perpendicular drops of the Scottish Highlands, hurtled down the pretty manicured slopes of Switzerland and ambled through the yellow hills of Austria and into the rubble of Rome. I had sailed across the Channel, rested on the quiet poppy fields of Belgium, passed the headiness of Amsterdam, passed the pomp of Paris, crossed the hillocks of Germany and onto the seaside and shoreline of Spain. I had watched the sun rise and set over the Greek Islands. Further eastwards, I had crossed the Iron Curtain into the former Balkan states. I had seen the city of minarets in Istanbul, and travelled through Transoxiana following the ancient caravanserai of the silk route across the grey plains and sacked cities of Central Asia. I had bussed through the ancient steppe land of the Stan countries on to the fertile plains and northern belts of Iran. Across the vast desert tracts of the Middle East, I had passed nomadic tribes and cacti, passed coastlines where fishermen once dived into waters for pearls and entered the pristine modernity of the Gulf States, before journeying back to the old ruins and rocks of Syria and Lebanon. I had travelled through the Sahara Desert and the sandy Atlas Mountains of North Africa, through the dense jungles of Central Africa and into the quiet vineyards and nature reserves of South Africa. I had lain on white Caribbean beaches, picked starfish from the clear cool seabed and danced the merengue on catamarans out in the ocean while mariners sang. I had travelled through America's heartland, craned my neck at the skyscrapers of the towering commercial cities before escaping into the jungles and waterfalls of the Latin countries, cycling through the lush paddy fields of Thailand, past the flashing lights of Tokyo and into the remote Korean mountainside dotted with its stone Buddhas. To so many countries I had travelled. And like the returning swallow, I had turned full circle and come back again.

And yet ... and yet, it was not enough. I would have given it all up ... yes, I would have given it all up ... for my Valley. How could I make them understand? My Valley. My beautiful little Valley. If only I could return.

One day Papa asked me a question. 'Liyana, we have grown up and lived in Kashmir, but you were born and brought up in England. Tell me, why is it that you feel so strongly about Kashmir?'

The question was a valid one and one I thought long and hard about. After all, there had been other people, many others in fact, like my grandfather who had lived in Kashmir all their lives and lost it too. Surely their claim would always be greater than mine? What was it about that small patch of earth that stirred such strong emotions in me?

I could not answer Papa's question properly. I did not know where to begin.

'How can I explain it, Papa?'

Even in the Valley, I occupied a strange status. I was neither local nor foreigner. Once a *rickshaw-wallah* quoted me the tourist rate for a journey and I protested.

'But I'm not a tourist!'

The *rickshaw-wallah* had been obstinate though and seeing no alternative I relented and got in. But while he was driving, something compelled me and I began pouring my heart out, telling him how my parents were Kashmiri and how I came to be born and brought up in England.

'There I'm not English. Here I'm not Kashmiri. I belong nowhere!'

The *rickshaw-wallah* listened bemused. I guess he was probably more concerned about the fare, but in the end he just shrugged and told me, 'It's okay. I know you're Kashmiri.'

I paid him the foreigner rate anyway.

'How can I explain it, Papa?' It was not quantifiable. That place gave me something that three-month single-entry visas and immigration stamps failed to give me, something that the newspaper people who wrote about citizenship and identity in the country of my birth failed to understand. I struggled to find the words. Kashmir was something I could not shake off, something I could not just cast aside. It was an eternal invitation.

Somehow as soon as I stepped out there, I knew. Somehow, I just knew. The wandering stopped there. It was like returning to something. Somewhere out there in those rolling hills, among the apple trees and rose bushes, it was within reach. That one house I kept returning to.

The White House.

146

That place of fairy tales.

I knew I had felt it in the White House, that powerhouse of the senses, that factory of love from which everything began and to which everything returned, the key to everything, the source of it all. I knew it was the White House that led me back to that place. There had been something about that place, something about the way the wild birds gathered on the broken gables during the day and the little spiders, hidden in the grass, crawled out onto the walls at night. The love … there had been a colossal love that stemmed from that place and I had felt it there when I was a child. I had felt part of something, something greater. I felt it each time I returned. There was no placard, no welcome sign, no homecoming parade. There were no lines in the earth. It went beyond that. Our histories ran much deeper. They had been mapped to memory. It was as natural as exhalation and inhalation, as natural as the migrating birds circling back to the warmer plains for spring. There was something about that place that had left its mark on me. It ran far deeper than physical lineaments and features, far deeper than the fair skin, the tall nose and the green eyes. Its imprints were intangible. I just knew there was a part of me that was only me because of Kashmir.

'I feel it right here,' I told my grandfather, placing my hand on my chest suddenly feeling disheartened.

No one else seemed to understand and it hurt trying to explain. It was something I felt, rather than reasoned.

'It's as if I cannot show you the way, Papa. I can only tell you when I reach there.'

I paused and looked at my grandfather, deflated, trying to see if he had understood. He was quiet but I could tell from the expression on his face that I had succeeded.

At Morad's home, there were no front gardens along the road

unlike the open, leafy entrances that marked the properties on Alderton hill. The houses on the street were modest abodes and ran shoulder to shoulder in a uniform line all the way down to the junction, with low gates marking the entryways to each property. From top to bottom, cars lined the pavement on either side. His parents had left early that morning on their coach-trip. Three out of four of his elder sisters were married and no longer living at the home and the youngest one was out. It was just the two of us, alone. Standing outside that house for the first time, a small wave of emotion overcame me as I realised I'd been waiting for this moment for so long. How many years had I longed to be welcomed into this home? How much had I heard about the people who lived inside and felt privy to their lives and dreams? I was finally being let in.

Morad took out his keys to unlock the door. But at the doorstep, I faltered. Deep down, it did not feel right. It did not feel right at all. I could not deceive myself. I knew I was only there because everyone else was away. I looked up at Morad, hesitant. It felt almost conspiratorial, collusive, but already in too deep I found my doubts following his steps inside. I slipped in uncomfortably, all at once awkward and shy.

The home was modest and functional. It was an old building and the age was beginning to show along the extremities. In one of the rooms, the corners of the wallpaper had started to peel and the carpet had come away from the edge exposing the floorboards underneath. A loose plank creaked noisily, making me feel even clumsier and more out of place.

'The flooring needs a bit of cover-up work,' he explained. 'I'll get round to it soon.'

Upstairs, I counted one room for his parents, another two for his sisters, and further up another little narrow stairwell, cut off from the rest of the house, a small attic space that was his room. I wondered where the other two sisters had lived when they had all been under the same roof.

148

Climbing the little narrow stairwell to the top, I imagined small feet pattering up the steps and could not help thinking that Morad's room reminded me of a small boy's play-loft. I recalled the stories he told me about his younger years of playing upstairs with the other children while his parents chatted away with aunts and uncles downstairs. In my childhood, lofts were always used to store a treasure-trove of playthings like board games, frisbees, old bicycles and Lego. If we were lucky, sometimes Leila and I would come across a ping-pong table or a dartboard hidden from view.

It must have been an oasis for a small boy, but the room struck me as strangely cramped for a young man of Morad's age. The windowless walls curved inwards, with only a small roof-opening that let in a thin shaft of light. Several photographs of the family stood dotted about haphazardly, upright like soldiers. The bed took up much of the room. A green and red flag hung from one side of the cupboard, half-draped over its headboard. Perhaps Morad saw my eyes wandering or suddenly grew conscious, because he would not let me linger there for long. He ushered me to the window, pulling it ajar, and jumped up onto the ledge before squeezing himself through the opening. He seemed happy and playful, almost boyish. From the rooftop, he extended his arm and beckoned me to join him. I took his hand. He pulled me up and led me into the sunshine outside.

In the afternoon sun, we sat dangling our feet over the edge, looking out across the grassy, slightly overgrown backyard before us. In one corner of the garden was a small vegetable patch. The beds were overcrowded with plants and herbs. A chilly bush and several tomato plants protruded through a spray of mint flowers. The garden was messy but so green, a leaf of the Bangladesh he had described to me. A worn football peeked from among the tall grasses. Vines had grown all around the boundary fencing, closing the garden in even more. As I took in the clear blue sky, I remember thinking how small and sad that garden suddenly appeared, how different from the large, capacious outback I grew up in. I thought of Leila, so far from me now, and how we used to play for hours at the back of our garden, how no one disturbed us. It was just the two us alone. I watched a white plastic bag parachute up in the breeze before hitting the back of the fence over and again and glum thoughts clouded my head. All at once I felt desperately trapped.

Morad looked over to me and from beneath those dark lashes he smiled, jolting me out of my unhappiness. His hand moved gently towards mine and took my fingertips in his. He seemed happy, perfectly content in that small world and it suddenly struck me it would be an injustice taking him from it. He was so connected to it, so alive in it. I gave a lukewarm smile, not wanting to ruin the moment and tried to conceal the sadness filling me inside.

Although he spoke of his community and his life among them, I knew Morad would never let me see them. He kept me perpetually apart. The very possibility of my existence seemed to threaten them. It threatened everything they held most dear.

'You don't understand because you don't have a community.'

That was the line always thrown back at me. But I had tried hard to understand. I had come to appreciate that for Morad his hidden community was this incorporeal thing upheld since childhood. He had not come into the world naked and alone, he had come clothed in something treasured and timeless. More precious than any inheritance of land or wealth was this thing that he had. It was as close as the umbilical cord that connected him to his mother, as sacrosanct as his faith. It was something pure, something inviolable, something that needed to be protected for it held everything together, it connected him to others and it told him who he was.

But I never saw it.

I never met them, I never saw them, I never spoke to

them, but this invisible community suffocated me with its absence. It threw a spotlight on my longing and turned it sour. When news found its way back to me through a lattice of sources, that the community had condemned me as some '*Pakistani furi!*' (Pakistani girl), '*shada furi*' (white girl), '*orthor modeern fureen*' (one of those modern girls) that Morad was seeing, my heart sank. I had been cast out. It was as if these people had drawn a red circle around me like the woman at the Indian visa counter, and I felt an excruciating sense of alienation.

The more I appreciated Morad's immersion in his community and his ability to return to it at will, the more I saw reflected back to me my own longing to belong and my separation from it. Bit by bit, a hardness began to build inside me. It barricaded my insecurities and hurt feelings and the more he kept me away, the more it festered. Each time he conversed with them and I could not understand, each time he went to them and I could not follow, each time he chose them over me, the hardness grew more entrenched, more permanent. Even the visits to the cultural evenings grew insidious. I could never go with him. Whenever I thought of them, I was reminded of the immigration desks, the border controls and checkpoints. I was reminded of the visa stamps that reduced individuals to no more than ticks in a box, the barbed wire that twisted the fate of ordinary people and the maps that tore up the earth. I wanted to burn them all.

Community began to morph into something else. It became something that forced Morad's hand. It was a collective guilt. It meant the swaddling clothes of the past that straight-jacketed the future. It was an anchor that held him back. Community became this intimidating adversarial force disapproving and frowning on everything it did not know. It survived only by inculcating a fear and paranoia of its own annihilation. It built walls around me. It made me a victim of cruel customs. When Morad insisted it was impossible for him to

151

talk to his community about me, it actually felt as if it physically muted him. It incapacitated him. It made him powerless without understanding why.

In the end, community was something that broke my trust. It was something that separated Morad from me. It separated me from his family. It meant telling you what you were not. It was a closed members' club, more difficult to get into than the most prestigious country club. It was a bolted heart. It kept you out.

As the grip of his community grew stronger and more relentless, I found myself forced into the margins. Bit by bit, I was pushed further away. Our brief evenings together lapsed into passing cups of tea. Our conversations became truncated, frustrated affairs. Perfunctory hugs replaced kisses. The absences grew more extended, the time spent together, less. Still, Morad refused to let me in. He would try to explain, try hard to comfort me, taking me on long sad drives through the city at night when everyone else was asleep as if hoping to assuage my loneliness by extending his car as a temporary home when there was nowhere else to go. And side by side together only artificially, we would drive aimlessly through that sad illusion, pretending to run away as we coursed through the city's backstreets getting lost in the dark, straining to cling onto our better memories even as they slipped through our hearts.

As the years passed, I found myself sitting passively listening to the same strains of thought played out over and again in that closed space like an unhappy refrain. Confined to my seat, Morad tried to placate me with explanations and justifications, hoping to convince me, telling me again and again it was because I lacked a community that I could not understand, barely realising that those words merely added salt to the wound inside. But somehow those outpourings seemed to give him a sense of tranquillity, some reassurance and validation, and so in the end I would let them run uninterrupted. Perhaps they lent more comfort to him. After a while, I no longer needed to hear the words to understand what was being said and I found myself switching off and just gazing at him quietly from the passenger seat. When the light played against his face the lines of passion animated his soft features and I would drift away from the conversation and my head would fill with inoffensive thoughts like how he had the most beautiful, long eyelashes or how he had the most perfectly sculpted brow, and in those moments I would remember the words my mother had taught me when I was a child, when she sat by my bedside at night and told me how God had made us all into different tribes so that we might get to know one another. And in the dark, tears trickled down my cheek falling onto my lap unnoticed as I wondered why it had to be so difficult.

I knew Morad loved me. Deep down, I knew a part of him realised he was hurting me. On occasion, he'd catch me staring at him in the car and a peaceful smile would break over his face and for a few seconds a beautiful stillness would settle between us. His eyes implored mine, and he would reach over taking my hand in his, wrap his fingers around mine, and I would see my paleness contrasted against his brown skin as he clasped my palm even more tightly, fighting back his own grief.

'No one else fits so perfectly in my embrace, Liyana,' he assured me. 'Isn't that a sign from God that we've been crafted for one other?'

Not once did I doubt him. But the tranquillity would never last. The vibrations of my longings were too subtle to be properly understood, and the pull of his other life too far for me to grasp. Out of ignorance, impatience, or perhaps a willing self-deception, my desires were misunderstood and discarded. After some time, the same unhappy refrain always started up again and he would continue despondently, creasing his brow once more.

With Morad, I saw a boy torn between two worlds. Perhaps, the world his community offered was a better world for him. Perhaps it was an older, more revered world. But it was a world that forgot his reality. Like the medieval moats and drawbridges that filled my textbooks at school, it bore no resemblance to the world we lived in.

And it forgot me.

Perhaps he told himself that one day he would tell them. One day, he would have the courage to confront them and everything would come together seamlessly and redeem all the hurt that took place before, the sharp edges of pain smoothed out into happy reunion, the sorrow finally chiselled away. But until then, he continued implacably, carrying the full weight of a worldview that accepted it was inevitable our lives would never meet. Until then, he kept the two worlds spinning on separate plates, perhaps already half-knowing it was only a matter of time before one of them dropped.

When Morad left for Bangladesh that summer, I did not suspect anything, nothing out of the ordinary, nothing that made me question or think anything was amiss. I suppose I just assumed it was another trip, no different from the rest. We met the day before he left for the airport and embraced. His body pressed close against mine as he wrapped his arms around me. I felt the warmth of his flesh as he kissed me, breathing me in. He tightened his grip, clasping me against his chest and the unexpected passion took me by surprise.

'Just checking you're still real,' he smiled when he saw my reaction, brushing the moment aside.

He kissed me gently on the forehead and then released me. It had felt real, so very real. As he made his way to the car, he turned and smiled again. Those large mysterious eyes reached out to mine. Maybe he wanted to tell me something. The dark globes shimmered, but I thought nothing of it. He always had such impenetrable, deep eyes. I waved goodbye as his car drove off into the distance.

In his absence, the city overtook me once again. I let it subsume me and carry me back through its arteries into anonymity. In the office, the hours came and went. I worked without pause, continuing into the early hours, counting down the days for his return. A week passed. Two weeks passed. No news.

Three weeks passed. Still no news. I tried to contact him. No phone calls. No emails. No letters. I reached out again and again. Four weeks passed. Five. I called his office only to be informed that no one by his name worked at the firm anymore.

'There must be a mistake,' I insisted. 'Would you mind checking the directory again, please? There must be a mistake.'

But there was no mistake. The records were correct. He had gone. It was as if every trace that might have led me back to Morad had been erased. There was nothing left, like he had never existed at all.

Eventually, I could bear it no longer and decided to visit his home.

It was evening. The clocks had been turned back that morning and it was already getting dark. The sky was grey. I hailed a cab from the office and gave the driver the address. As we drove, the rain beat down and the wipers whirred against the windscreen despondently and I remember looking out and thinking how the colour matched my mood. Even inside the car, I could feel the cold, and as we made our way eastwards I asked the driver to turn up the heating. It felt so cold.

Our car came off the junction and kneaded its way down a slip-road, passing two sets of traffic lights. I recognised the landmarks. The duck ponds where Leila and I used to throw bread crusts in the summers. The pub with its wooden benches where my friends congregated after school. The old cricket lawns. Even the rickety lane that led to the tennis centre where we trained day after day. Behind every stone, there was a secret story.

But driving through those familiar haunts in the rain, everything I saw seemed strangely dated, as if I was looking out through a black and white negative still. The cab reached the station and before I knew it an endless line of terraced homes came into view. I recognised them instantly. Old Station Road.

As we turned into the junction, a large signboard up ahead caught my attention. At first, I mistook it for a billboard. I was sure it had not been there the last time I visited Morad's home. Was it a blank sign … or was I mistaken? I was mistaken.

Dark lines cut up the perfect whiteness. Four capital letters stared blankly back at me: *SOLD*.

Behind them, I made out the shadowy outline of the house I had come to visit. Morad's car was nowhere to be seen. A sickness began to seep into my gut and I wanted to go back. But something impelled me and I got out of the car. The lights in the neighbouring house were on and I could see the silhouette of a man moving about in the front room. I needed to know. Involuntarily, I made my way through the dark to the porch.

I rang the bell, waiting, desperately waiting for someone to answer. It was raining in large drops. An elderly man unfastened the latch and opened the door. I caught a whiff of curry and coconut smells. Behind him, the sound of a television blared out in a foreign language. I was at a loss, stammering through a series of convoluted apologies before addressing the source of my pain.

'The house next door … the house next door … what has happened to the people in the house next door?'

The man must have seen the anguish on my face for he looked surprised, concerned even. I suddenly realised I knew who he was. Morad had told me about him. He was the neighbour who organised the coach-trips each year. His wife had passed away of cancer last year and ever since then he had been nursing a broken heart. With a cruel twinge, I realised he knew nothing about me. I mustered a weak smile.

'Hasan *Sahib's* family?' He gestured with his hands, before giving me the explanation I had been so wretchedly wanting to know. 'Bangladesh. Son gone for marriage ...'

An invisible fist punched me in the stomach. For several moments, I stood there winded. I was numb. I was broken. Morad had left me. He had left me. I let the full enormity of that desertion rip through me. It wrung through my insides. Perhaps I should have felt angry. Perhaps I should have felt betrayed. I should have felt hurt. But the only emotion that filled me as I stood outside that dark house was one of loneliness. Wave upon wave of loneliness. I had never felt so alone. Whatever else the neighbour said, I cannot remember.

There was something special about London's taxis, and the attraction was more than that they were free from the office after nine o'clock at night. I used to look forward to seeing them parked outside the building in the evenings, their white name-boards calling out to various passengers. They were always there, a cluster of them, waiting faithfully by the rank like beacons of solace to take you home. To his passenger, the taxi driver was a friend, a confidante, a faceless, nameless stranger who spoke and listened but never judged. At times, I think there were patches in the city when I spoke more openly to those drivers than to any other person during the day. Maybe it was the thought of going home that lent a certain comfort, for each time I sank into those leather seats I found myself unravelling like a coil. With each driver, it was like a flame being lit. The match would flare up for a few moments of interaction before finally extinguishing and each of us moved on. But somehow, with each trip, each exchange, my chest felt a little lighter, as if purged in those mobile confessional booths. It never seemed necessary to see the face of the person I confided in. Sometimes it felt like I was just talking to a disembodied voice. And yet those voices were some of the most memorable I heard during that time. Never before had I paused to appreciate the diversity of London's taxi drivers. The cabs ferried across so much human traffic, they became natural repositories for the countless stories of the people who passed through the city.

There was the taxi driver with the cockney accent. As soon as he received the passenger information and saw my name, he was curious to know where I came from.

'Suuk–suurkaa–Suuk–arr–warr–di? Is that right? Now with a name like that, lady, I gotta ask where you're from.'

When I returned the question, he began telling me about his life, how he had been born and bred in East London, and how his father and grandfather had lived there all their lives too. He came from a working class family and had worked hard to rise out of estate life, but he owned his own home now, and had three sons. The youngest was seventeen and he wanted him to go to university. He made sure that his son studied hard and was never hanging around the street corners like the other local kids.

'None of my boys do that,' he told me and I sensed the pride of a father.

He was interested to know where my name came from, thinking perhaps I might have been Iranian. He had many Iranian clients and always welcomed foreigners to the city.

'Never know where the poor bugger's come from,' he explained.

And then I met an Afghan driver. I recognised the soft-sounding language the instant he spoke into his headset. I had heard that same mellifluous accent before. I asked him where he came from, half-guessing the answer already. When I told him my parents came from Kashmir, he repeated the word back to me and sighed.

'Kashmir. Beautiful. But place sad, like my country.'

And then the thought struck me and I wondered what he thought of England, this low-lying island so far from the mountainous regions where he had grown. Did he feel as foreign and out of place as I felt when I was in the Valley? Did he ever think about the life he left behind? I wondered whether he carried the same hopes and dreams to England as I carried to Kashmir. Had they all been shattered like mine?

He slowly unfolded his story, and I listened in part disbelief as he insisted he'd once been a fighter-jet pilot but traded it all in many years ago to come to England. When he first arrived in the city, he worked in Hackney for several years trying to convince a bevy of Jamaican ladies that his family had washed laundry for generations. He laughed reminiscing. He was doing okay as a taxi driver in London, but sometimes he wished he could go back, go back home. It was almost impossible now. It had always been his dream to fly planes in the sky, he confided, ever since he was a small boy. I listened to his tales with intrigue, trying to map his story against history. He did not seem young, maybe in his late forties, I could not be sure. Perhaps he enjoyed telling people his story or perhaps he had no one else to tell it to for he seemed sad when I paused in my questions.

'Don't stop,' he urged. 'This journey will soon be over.'

When his cab eventually pulled up outside my apartment, he turned around to say goodbye and I saw he had the most striking blue eyes. They were sparkling, like the reflection of light on water.

And how could I forget the little old lady who had been driving taxis for over forty years. She must have been in her seventies, almost as old as Ami. She had a kind, sympathetic voice and when I first heard her greeting, I suddenly wanted to know everything about her. I told her that I had never met a female taxi driver before.

'Oh,' she began in a warm, smiling voice. 'Oh, there are still a few of us about, dear.'

Sitting in that London cab, I suddenly realised how little I knew of the lives of the people all around me. It dawned on me

159

there were swirls of people who I passed, day after day, again and again, who went by unacknowledged and ignored. On the tube, waiting at the bus stop, in restaurants and coffee shops, walking along the overpass, or down Glengali Street with the school runs. The man who turned up late for his appointment at the dentist. The woman pushing her pram in Poplar Park with no child. The couple seated beside me on the DLR westbound line to Tower Gateway. Who were those people? And what were their stories? And what about my loved ones? What about my family, what did I really know of them? My grandparents, my mother, my father. How could I contain them or grasp them or hold them? How could I possibly understand them? They were boundless, vessels of so many stories. The sequence of thought came to its inevitable resting place.

Morad.

And what about Morad? What about the one person I had wanted to know everything about? How little in the end I knew about him.

Inside the taxi, the cabin was noiseless and calm. I rested my head against the glass pane, looking out into the vast black, satiny cloth of the night as the universe returned my gaze. The sleet was falling hard outside, gliding down the pane. As the water tried to settle, each time it was interrupted by new droplets and different patterns formed. I watched the globules of water land on the glass and change shape, comforted.

I was not alone.

Perhaps one day we will meet again.

Yes, perhaps one day we will meet again, in new faces and new places, and this time we will love those hearts again for what mattered and not for the rest. We will learn from broken things. Perhaps only then will we be able to inherit old worlds without being subsumed in them. Only then will we be able to create new worlds with new possibilities. Worlds without borders. Worlds of love. Worlds we can share and still call our own. Looking out into the night I etched my longings in the sky and I left them there. As our cab ploughed into the darkness, I watched the landscape melt … the street lights blur … the moon flicker.

'May I ask you a question?' a gentle voice inquired a little hesitantly from the front seat as we pulled into my drive. 'You have such a wonderful name, dear. Where are you from?'

I turned from the window, stirred back to the present, and spoke to the voice coming from the driver's seat.

'I'm from here,' I told her, and left the cab smiling.

The deal was almost closed. I spent the whole night trawling through paperwork at my desk, finalising the last details. The day arrived. I had not been home since the previous morning and was in need of rest. It was almost over. Others had worked through the night too and as soon as the transaction was complete, they headed out to drown themselves in a nearby bar. I gave my excuses although there had been no need. Everyone knew why.

As I stepped out through the sliding doors, a wave of sunshine washed over me and I instantly felt the warmth glide through my body. The sun was shining in London. It was a beautiful day. A group of girls wearing oversized sunglasses crossed in front of me chattering away excitedly to one another, completely oblivious to the fact they had almost walked into me. All around, I saw the city folk, spread out, eating their lunchtime sandwiches, soaking up the good weather. Their faces held that expression that comes to the face of every Londoner when the sun finally makes an appearance, a contented forgiving smile as if that one day of sunshine was enough to expiate the drudgery of a whole year of bad climate. It made the idea of heading towards the underground station and returning to a dingy, artificially-lit world seem absurd.

161

I wandered aimlessly around the city, not really paying attention to my direction but not really caring either. I had never taken the time to stroll through the city by day and I allowed myself to become lost in the maze of streets and shops. I drifted through Old Spitalfields Market, ambling into the textile outlets of Commercial Street, passing the Town Hall on my way. I left Aldgate East station behind and walked down Whitechapel Road, continuing past a yellow tip stacked to the brim with cardboard and metal scraps. Several minutes later, I was stunned to find myself standing outside the same park Morad took me to on our first evening together. I had never realised it was so close.

In the daylight, I saw the green was called Altab Ali Park. It struck me as an unusual name for an English park and I was immediately curious to know who Altab Ali was. I spotted a garden caretaker.

'He was a young Bengali fellow. Poor chap was murdered some time back in a racist attack.'

Ali was only twenty-five at the time and had been working in the area as a textile worker. The park commemorated the site of his last walk home when he was set upon by a gang of white youths and brutally murdered. It had been renamed after the incident. There in the corner, I saw the replica of the *Shaheed Minar*. The mother and her martyred sons. As I looked out at that symbol, thinking how I would probably never see the original monument in Dhaka now, something gave way and I thought of my first drive through the city with Morad.

London had never seemed more vast and beautiful than on that first night together. And I remembered how we had chased the lights along the Thames and crisscrossed playfully over the different bridges trying to work out which one gave the prettiest view of the capital's skyline, laughing all the way down to the East End, how he had taken my hand in his own and wrapped his fingers around mine protectively as we drove, and how amazed I had been to see the Jewish bagel shop nestled among the curry houses on Brick Lane. Wherever we went, the colours had shone out like lanterns in the dark, light on light. We rested there. We stopped there. We paused in those places together. And then this park.

I remembered the last time I saw Morad and our final goodbye, how tightly he had held onto me, refusing to let go. Perhaps he had always known.

A group of city folk started to spread themselves out on the grass. On a bench behind them, an elderly Bengali man sat down to rest. A toddler clutched a melting ice-cream in his small chubby fist and waddled towards a pigeon. As I watched I wondered what Morad was doing, and I wondered if somewhere, out there, he was happy. It is odd. He probably never knew. I remember thinking perhaps first love is something like that. Perhaps it is something that could have happened but never happened sometime long ago.

It did not feel right standing in that park anymore. I lingered for a moment, eavesdropping on time, long enough to see underfoot along the path running down the centre of the park a trail of metallic letters spelling out a line from one of Tagore's poems: *THE SHADE OF MY TREE IS OFFERED TO THOSE WHO COME AND GO FLEETINGLY.*

Not long after, a glamorous Pakistani politician made an eagerly anticipated diplomatic trip to Delhi, sporting the same Hermes Birkin handbag I had seen Leila wear. The national press greeted her with sugary smiles and wolf-whistles. Less than a month later, my visa for India came through, and I returned to the Valley, alone.

In Srinagar, my uncle welcomed me at the airport and in his embrace I quickly forgot the complications that had prevented me from returning sooner. I continued as before. I returned to the market coffee shops. I went jogging around the lake. In the city, I met up with the boys from our basketball team. I was passing by the grounds of the old school when they recognised me.

'Ma'am! Ma'am!'

I turned in surprise, at first not registering who they were. They looked so different, almost men now. Back then, I was not yet twenty, and the boys were barely in their teens. They took me to a nearby coffee shop that had recently opened downtown and I ordered a perfect Italian cappuccino, although it felt strange doing so. The boys told me they were studying at university. Growing up had made them restless. They told me in earnest of their dreams of leaving the Valley and going abroad, but how these aspirations worried their parents. Their families feared that once they ventured out of the Valley they might never return and so they tried to distract them with matters at home. But it only drew the opposite effect, intensifying their resolve to see the outside world. Several of them had already offered their papers and applied for passports.

'One day we will come to England, Ma'am,' the youngest one declared confidently. 'And when we do, we will marry pretty English girls!' he added cheekily as an afterthought.

I laughed, wondering what the boys would think of England. Their sharp features and striking eyes were certain to attract a horde of admirers. The youngest had a small diamante stud in his ear and seemed heavily affected by fashion and Brazilian football players. But when the conversation turned to girls, I was amazed to discover how innocent they still were.

'Sometimes I wonder, how I will ever know how to kiss a girl,' the youngest complained despondently to his friends. 'Once I even went onto YouTube to learn and I was like, what the hell are you doing man?'

One of the boys turned to me and asked if I had ever kissed someone. It was an awkward question and, conscious of the uncomfortable age gap between us and the differences

164

between the Valley and England, I pussyfooted around it. But the boys were so guileless and naive, and the question so natural and inquisitive, in the end, I relented.

'Yes,' I started uneasily. 'Yes … with someone very special. Someone I thought I was going to marry.' I paused. 'But it was always the kisses on the forehead that meant the most. Those are the ones I miss the most.'

The boy nodded thoughtfully. 'I guess it's a bit like when your grandmother kisses you on the forehead. You can tell how much she loves you.'

I smiled back pensively. I had never thought of it that way before, but I guess he was right.

'Yes.' I nodded slowly. 'Yes. Something very much like that.'

'*Agar firdous bar-ru-e-zamin ast; hamin asto, hamin asto, hamin asto*! If there is Paradise on earth, it is here, it is here, it is here!' My uncle smiled. 'Why would I ever want to leave?'

I was examining the photographs plastered about his lounge and asked why he had not left the Valley. After all, the White House was gone. Why had he chosen to stay on? I did not understand. Why, when he could have escaped so long ago?

The walls of his living room were cluttered with photo-frames. Hundreds of different pictures of all shapes and sizes hung on the sides. Among them, I recognised the faces of my cousins in America, Germany and Canada. We had all once played together outside the White House, hiding in places we could not be found. But they had left the Valley long ago. At the beginning, I suppose, they must have not expected to stay away for long, but the troubles kept them from returning and I guess over time other parts proved kinder. Eventually, they set up their homes elsewhere. Some of the pictures were quite dated now. I knew my cousins were no longer the shiny-eyed youngsters smiling out from those frames. They had grown up now. Most of them were married, some even had children of their own. Even my uncle's daughter had emigrated to America many years ago.

I spotted images of my uncle's grandchildren, my nephews and nieces; the latest additions to the family. All of them had been born abroad. Through the swirling mass of coloured print on plaster I mapped out various marriages and births, trips to Disney Land, school sports days, birthday parties, safari holidays to Africa. Grinning, happy toddlers in soccer shirts and baseball caps frozen in frames. Most of them had probably never visited the Valley, never seen the house. I wondered if they ever would. Years on, what would this ghostly land mean to them? And what would they know of this cindery home, except the stories we chose to pass on?

I paused, lost in my thoughts. But perhaps by then, it would no longer be the resting place that it once was for us. Perhaps, by then, there would be other memories, other homes.

I found several older pictures mixed in with the new. One picture in particular stood out, slightly elevated above the rest. It was a faded grey photograph. A man sits beside a woman with solemn expression, turbaned and stately in flowing white robes. My grandparents passed away many years ago, long before I had the chance to know them. The living room was like a small shrine to an absent family.

I turned to face my uncle and saw he had been watching me for some time. As our eyes locked, he smiled.

'Why would I ever want to leave, Liyana?' he repeated gently as if knowing something I did not. 'Why, when everything good in the world can grow here?'

On my last night in the Valley, I stayed overnight in one of the border towns, somewhere deep in the mountains. My driver told me that once a great war had been fought here and many young

166

men had died fighting along the alpine passes. At the outpost, we passed a familiar caution: *WARNING! YOU ARE UNDER ENEMY OBSERVATION.*

It was nightfall by the time we arrived and as soon as I stepped from the jeep, I was plunged into darkness. It took a few moments for my vision to adjust. Beyond the dimly lit street, lay nothing but stillness. The buildings that lined either side of the road were low-lying and crumbling into rubble. They looked like abandoned storehouses. Even the glass panes of the windows were broken. Everything seemed in ruins and I imagined standing in a wasteland, amidst the wreckage of Guernica, Sarajevo or Hiroshima after the bombs had fallen.

A young boy sat idly on one of the windowsills looking out to nothing in particular. His body was half-shadowed and leaning out into the night. I thought of a black sunflower reaching towards the moon. Several men crouched on the pavement. The people here possessed features I had never seen anywhere else. Their faces were neither Asian nor European. I could not place them. They seemed a multiplicity of different ethnicities all at once, as if the whole of humanity had mixed in this frontier town. I drifted along in the darkness feeling like I had arrived at the ends of the earth. The entire world seemed to compress into a single dark street. I was a stranger, just a traveller on the road. The realisation hit me with a searing intensity. There was something utterly terrifying and yet simultaneously liberating about it. Maybe all border towns made you feel this way.

The next morning I left the township behind and went on foot further up into the mountains, crossing through the brambles and thickets as I followed the shepherd trails, going deeper and deeper into the heights. At one point, I lost my grip and fell. The terrain was steep and difficult, but I carried on regardless, not knowing where the path would lead. Bit by bit the settlement below grew smaller retreating from view, before eventually passing under fog and disappearing entirely. I stopped looking back and continued on my way, stumbling over the broken stony tracks. The air grew quieter. Even the birdsong ceased. I could hear my own breathing.

I must have come through the other side of a cloud because all at once a huge expanse opened up before me and the earth was covered in a hazy white light. The skyline was bare. A shepherd and a boy herded a flock nearby. They moved along effortlessly, coming closer. The altitude started catching up with me. Dizziness struck. I paused and rested on one of the rocks, and watched the flock pass.

I took in my surroundings. I had reached a huge alpine meadow, surrounded on all sides by a chain of tall mountains. Apart from the shepherd and the boy, I was alone. The flock moved closer and before long all I could hear was the sound of sheep nibbling on grassy pastures. There must have been at least several hundred sheep. Some were so close, their fleece brushed my legs. I felt the press of soft woolly bodies, and breathed in the musty smell of mountain sheep.

At the shepherd's whistle, they moved along. A few had short curved horns. The brown and black ones stuck out in the mass of whiteness. One by one they hurdled a small brook. One lamb became ensnared in a piece of metal wiring as it tried to make the crossing. It fell behind the rest of the group, bleating plaintively. Blood ran from along the barbed wire and into the water. As the shepherd herded the rest of the flock to the other side, he seemed instinctively to sense something was wrong. He returned to the brook, bent down, gently picked up the creature, and carried it over his shoulders to safety like it was a lost child.

As the flock continued moving along, the shepherd came to rest on a nearby rock and looked my way. Perhaps he was surprised to see a foreigner so high up in the hills, because he spoke, and though I could not fully understand the words he said, his eyes seemed to ask me where I came from. The little boy

168

stared at me in curiosity too, as if thinking I was not real. I could not respond in his native tongue so I pointed to the base camp at the bottom of the mountain, gesturing towards the small town below. Equally curious, I tried asking the shepherd where he was going. He pointed to a steep imposing mountain before us, and motioned towards the other side.

The mountain rose high into the sky. I shielded my eyes as I peered up, barely able to follow to the peak. We were close to the border and I was surprised, and signalled to ask whether he intended to cross. The man nodded.

There was a large alpine lake further up. India lay on one side and Pakistan on the other. I was confused knowing it would be perilous to make such a crossing and made exaggerated firing gestures to indicate danger, though I was not sure who from.

The boy laughed. The shepherd smiled and I was relieved to see he understood. It was okay, he reassured me. No one bothered them. I was suddenly struck by his courage. He told me it was very beautiful across the border, and he plucked a small flower from the ground and held it out.

'*Moch saara phol*' (many, many flowers), he said, explaining the presence of manifold different types of flowers growing on the other side.

We conversed between languages with broken gestures for a few moments longer, before the shepherd picked up his staff and began to make his way across the meadow. The boy followed, ushering the flock along with him. I accompanied the pair for a time, then on reaching the next clearing, I raised my hand and offered my goodbyes. The shepherd smiled and nodded his understanding. The boy lingered reluctantly, staring at me still, before finally turning too. He must have been no older than seven.

As my gaze followed him, I remembered my seventh birthday. The same day my mother told me about the Day of Judgement while we recited our prayers together at bedtime. It was the first time Leila and I learnt about it. That day when the sun becomes shrouded in darkness, when the stars collapse and fall in, and the mountains uproot themselves and every soul rises from the earth to appear naked once again before their Creator. On that day when no soul avails another in the least, neither is intercession accepted on its behalf, nor compensation taken from it, nor is it helped. I had started crying. I didn't want to be alone, I sobbed to my mother. I was afraid of being alone. My mother hugged me reassuringly.

'You can never be alone, Liyana. You can never be alone.'

It felt like a drop in time.

The two figures travelled up the steep ascents with the deftness of their flock. The boy was wearing worn oversized city shoes, totally unsuitable for the hostile mountain terrain, and I wondered whether he would be okay. In the distance, he seemed to sense my thoughts and looked back. The sound of the shepherd's whistling echoed in the air and I listened until the gentle rumble of warm bodies moving closely together over the earth quietened, and the herd gradually receded from view before dissolving into the horizon.

Slowly, I made my way down the mountain.

Back in the jeep, I pulled from my pocket the flower the shepherd had given. It was a tiny purple flower with dark inky blue veins on the petals. As I twirled it between my fingertips, quietly reminded of all the friendships I had made on my travels, I could not help smiling, thinking how wonderful it was to be able to live in a world without borders.

Returning from the Valley that last time, I stopped searching for Kashmir. For a long time I realised I had been searching for it and I had looked for it in vain.

My uncle once said, 'If you go into the mountains you

will see things that will change your life forever.'

I guess he was right, for somewhere deep in those mountains I witnessed something. I witnessed something extraordinary. And as that white light burned down melting the sky into the earth, blinding me with its perfect clarity, something deep inside gave way and I finally let go. I finally let go.

At that instant, the Valley answered my call at last, and from the depths of its core it seemed to sigh too, for a gust of wind swept through me, and as though a latch had been unfastened, the windows of my heart flung open and with them my memories released and flew out, flew out into the open, flew out into the wind, away from the hurt, the pain, the protracted drawn-out wait. My memories, oh my memories, they flew free.

On 16 May 2012, Shama Naqushbandi was granted a life-long visa to return to Kashmir. She would like to express her gratitude to all those who supported her in the process.

AUTHORS NOTE

My twin sister and I were born and raised in England. Our foreign-sounding names and fair skin always confused people and they would ask us where we came from. London never seemed to be the answer they were looking for, so we would tell them that we came from Kashmir. Most of the time, though, nobody knew where Kashmir was.

The title of this book was inspired by the name of my grandparents' home in Kashmir (pictured below) which I used to visit as a child before the conflict began. The house was eventually pulled down. Today, Kashmir remains site of one of the world's most militarised territorial disputes.

I write this book in memory of my beloved White House and for each and every child who has, at some point, struggled to answer the question 'Where am I from?'

Indigo Dreams Publishing
24 Forest Houses
Halwill
Beaworthy
Devon
UK
EX21 5UU